# A
# CUCKOO IN
# THE NEST

It is at the breakfast table that we join the irrepressible Peter Wykeham and his new wife, Sophia. Peter has just received a letter from Lady Bunter, an old family friend he has not seen since his Christening, who invites the newly wed couple for the weekend (and some shooting) at Rushcombe Fitz-Chartres, Somerset. Sophia is at first slightly apprehensive, but they decide eventually, as Peter's kedgeree gets cold, to go.

Their ostensibly peaceful weekend is not destined to pass without incident, however. It runs smoothly only as far as Paddington Station, where Peter misses the train – but Sophia does not. This unfortunate lack of time-keeping on Peter's part snowballs into a chain of events that is both hilarious and chaotic – a farrago of good intentions.

# A
# CUCKOO IN
# THE NEST

W. H. Allen · London
A Howard & Wyndham Company
1977

Printed and bound in Great Britain by

Butler & Tanner Ltd, Frome and London,
for the Publishers, W. H. Allen & Co. Ltd,
44 Hill Street, London W1X 8LB

ISBN 0 491 02102 X

'The Cuckoo is a bird that lays
other birds' eggs in its own
nest and viva voce.'
                Schoolboy's Essay

# Contents

# PART III
## 'GO HE MUST'

# PART ONE
## 'Come He Will'

# CHAPTER I

# Westward Ho!

Peter, after the manner of man at his breakfast table, had allowed half his kedgeree to get cold and was sniggering over a letter. Sophia looked at him sharply. The only letter she had received was from her mother. Sophia's mother was not a humorist.

'I've got a letter from some people I have often heard of but never met,' he explained, noticing her expression. 'Some people called Bunter.'

'Bunter? Do you mean the titled people who sent us an ornamental vase for a wedding present?'

'They are titled. He is Sir Stirling Bunter. They inherited it. As for the ornamental vase, I should say it's extremely likely. It seems to go, doesn't it – Sir Stirling and Lady Bunter, Ornamental Vase? I daresay they inherited that too. I've never set eyes on them, but they were old friends of my people and they've always kept up with me in a sort of way, if you know what I mean.'

'I'm afraid I don't quite,' said Sophia.

'Oh, yes, you do, dear. For instance they always, every year, send me Christmas cards; generally the awfully hearty sort of Christmas cards that people do send to other people that they don't know at all well. You know. The kind that have mottoes like

> Here's rattling good luck and roaring good cheer,
> With lashings of food and great hogsheads of beer.

And then, when you see the Bunters, you probably find that they are the most melancholy old folk with malignant diseases. I've always noticed that about Christmas cards.'

'But why do they write to you now? It isn't Christmas yet.'

'They don't both write. Fanny Bunter writes.'

'That's Lady Bunter,' commented Sophia for her own satisfaction.

He read the letter aloud. Sophia listened with the studied air of one for whom, even in these days, a title possesses some surreptitious allurement. During the three months of her married life she had often secretly admired and attempted, herself, to assume the genuine nonchalance of Peter in dealing with Bunters.

'My dear Peter,
    'It is ridiculous to think that we should not even know each other by sight. My husband and myself had intended to come to your wedding, but then found we couldn't. Still, the occasion served to remind us that the last time we set eyes on you was at your Christening. It makes me quite ashamed to think of, especially when I think that your dear parents would have counted on us to keep in touch with you. But we never come to London from year's end to year's end. It does not suit Stirling, and the last time he ventured there he had what might have been a most serious accident in a handsome cab.

'Handsome – *sic*,' commented Peter.

'Sick?'

'She thinks it was called a hansom-cab because it was good-looking, poor old dear. Never mind. Where are we – "handsome cab", yes':

    'At the time of your wedding we resolved to ask you to come and pay us a visit. I remember we did ask you once or twice before, but you have never been able to come. We are asking one or two friends to the house for the shooting and we shall be so pleased if you and your bride will join the party. Can you come on Thursday, the 18th of this

month, for a few days? I suppose you shoot. Your dear
father was such a good shot I know.

'With kindest regards,
'Yours very sincerely,
'FANNY BUNTER.'


'A very friendly letter,' said Sophia with suppressed
gratification. 'Where do these – Bunter people live?'

'At the Knoll, Rushcombe Fitz-Chartres, Somerset. One
moment':


'P.S. All our friends tell us that much the best train
down is the one that leaves Paddington just about one
o'clock. By this you only have to change at Bristol and
then at Glastonbury and then you get on to our little local
line. By the other train – the one in the morning – the
journey is supposed to be rather long and muddling.'


'Well,' said Sophia after a brief pause, 'why laugh?'

'I'm not laughing.'

'You were laughing to yourself over it.'

'Oh, was I? Perhaps I was a little tickled by the near thing
in the handsome. I wonder what the dear old soul would
think of our little turnout. By the way, dash it, Sophie, we
can't drive down there. These blighters say the car won't be
in running condition for a month.'

'Who said we wanted to drive down there?'

'If we don't want to,' said Peter, 'so much the better, because we can't. Unless of course we hire a car.'

Sophia stared. Such a suggestion seemed almost un-
principled to one who had been accustomed to hover on
kerbstones and fight for standing-room in the Chelsea
bus.

'Hire a car to go all that way?' she asked incredulously.

'I don't know. Why not?' replied Peter, watching her with
inquiring humility.

Sophia raised her eyebrows and pushed her chair back with a quick impulsive movement of the body.

'Are we going there at all is the first question,' she said.

'Yes,' said Peter.

'You seem very certain that I want to, I must say.'

'I don't at all. I simply meant "yes" about that being the first question.'

'I don't quite understand you. Are you going to eat that kedgeree? We haven't any other engagements that I know of, but should I like it there? Are they smart sort of people? Who will be there, do you suppose? I didn't know you shot. Do you shoot?'

Peter sat up to the table with the rather vacant smile of a man who appreciates the value of a secret grievance.

'I don't want my kedgeree. You would like it, I feel sure,' he began.

'I don't want it.'

'No, I mean the Bunters. I haven't a notion what sort of people are likely to be there. They are not smart at all, but County, don't you know? I shoot.'

Sophia hesitated. Peter's acquaintances were a very mixed assortment. Certain male specimens had put in an appearance at her wedding. Her mother had smelt them out like a witch doctor and had stigmatised them generally in two damning words, 'Fast fishes.' The female of this species of Peter's friends was understood to be more deadly even than the male and quite uninviteable, especially to his wedding. On the other hand, Sophia had discovered that Peter was on intimate terms with a large number of respectable, married personages, some of whom stood so high in the social scale that she found their patronage almost humiliatingly grateful.

With these people Peter enjoyed a magnificent assurance and ease of manner, which was the secret envy of his less confident bride. The vision of this country house party both enticed and embarrassed her. She carefully suppressed these feelings from Peter. And, when she came to think it over,

what had she to fear from any country house party? She had
a beautiful trousseau. And intelligence. Sir Stirling and Lady
Bunter – her mother would be pleased.

'All right,' she said.

'Oh, we are to go then?'

'Certainly. You seem keen and I'm quite willing to go.
Next Thursday week. We will go by the afternoon train as
Lady Bunter suggests.'

'Changing at Bristol and at Glastonbury to get on to the
little local line,' remarked Peter. 'The inferior morning train
must be first cousin to a Polar expedition.'

He rose from the breakfast table, submitted to a brief cat-
echism as to his programme for the morning, and went his
way.

Two months earlier he had returned to that specially consecrated flat from his honeymoon. He was the picture of
happiness, his bright young face was wreathed in smiles, his
fair hair waved from his forehead, he was plump and content as any bridegroom of twenty-four with an independence
– pecuniary – should be. To nobody but himself did he
confess that he had erred in his conception of what marriage
to Sophia held for him.

To himself he owned that before his marriage he had regarded Sophia as a sort of superior goddess, whom he could
enshrine in the consecrated flat and burn incense to whenever he felt so disposed. Instead he found himself settling
down, fairly happily, to be ruled. Peter had never been ruled
before. Even during the war he had been in the Air Force.

But, after all, a goddess ought to rule, and Sophia proved
herself deserving of incense. True, she demanded all the incense he had at his command. She had taken a very early
opportunity of showing him this quite clearly.

He had met a friend, a male friend, one of the male friends
who had been at the wedding. They still preyed upon him in
the window-seats of clubs and behind the swing-doors of
lounges, luring him back to intermittent confidences and
hurried, extemporaneous refreshment. Of this friend he had

inquired casually who was feeding Bobbie Kensington at the Piccadilly Grill nowadays. The friend had replied by insisting on Peter trotting down to Hammersmith Broadway to pay his respects to that queen of the front row chorus. A harmless episode; but at the consecrated flat tea and tenderness grew cold in company.

Peter returned, shamefaced at his dallying but quite frank as to his movements.

'You are never punctual,' said Sophia.

'I always am as a rule,' said Peter. 'Very punctual. As a matter of fact I am generally ahead of time. I am like the 6.30 edition of the evening papers. I am super-punctual.'

'Where have you been?'

He informed her cheerfully.

'Bobby Kensington? He sounds fast,' said Sophia with disapproval.

'It isn't Bobby, it's Bobbie,' said Peter. 'There's a wealth of difference. Bobbie, in the feminine, you know. As in – well, Tommie and Billie. I even seem to have heard of a Freddie somewhere.'

'You needn't think you are going to do that sort of thing now,' said Sophia.

'My dearest Sophie—'

'I daresay you used to mix with those sort of women before, but now—'

'I never mixed,' remonstrated Peter.

Bobbie, however, was ruled out firmly and finally. Peter bowed to the decision. His worship of Sophia grew but stronger for being enforced. Her unforeseen authority served merely to reinforce the spell of wonder and admiration which had constrained him ever since his first vision of her.

She was like a Beardsley *Salome*, he had said. And indeed she had the narrow eyes and the high cheekbone of that creation, and as nearly the sinuosity as is compatible with human symmetry. His wooing had been brief but incisive. He had carried off his prize in the teeth of unremitting opposition from Sophia's mother.

What this good lady's ambitions for her only child had been she never clearly defined. After receiving Peter Wykeham cordially in the first instance, as any fond mother should receive the suitor who pays his respects in a seven-hundred guinea runabout, Sophia's mother gradually cooled and finally froze completely. Unfortunately, however, for the determined lady, Sophia, who had inherited the determination, continued to favour Peter, and Sophia's father proved himself, as usual, pig-headed and unwilling to assert his authority, such as it was. Finally, after much vexed domestic wrangling, the frozen mother was thawed into an awe-inspiring maternal-bridal costume of dark lilac, and the parties were married early in June at St Peter's, Cranley Gardens.

'First stop Bristol. Take your seats, please,' said the guard, with an air of long-suffering authority, like that of the head-mistress of a large kindergarten.

'Take your seat, Peter,' echoed Sophia. 'I wonder why it is that men must always stand on the platform and look, just when their train is going.'

She spoke through the open door of their first-class carriage.

'I stand,' replied Peter, 'because one can't very well sit down in the middle of the platform; and I look to see why the bookstall girl hasn't given me all the papers I paid for.'

'Never mind that now. The train will go without you if you don't take care.'

'I'll take jolly good care it doesn't do that,' said Peter, fumbling with a disordered accumulation of journals. 'But where's my *Life*? Half a moment, Sophia. Just hang on to these, will you? I'm going back for my *Life*.'

'Nonsense. They're shutting the doors. Come into the carriage.'

'But my dear, I paid the girl. If she didn't mean me to see

*Life* she wouldn't have let me give her my ninepence. She didn't look that sort of girl at all.'

He bundled his collection of literature through the carriage doorway, and, turning, retraced his steps in the direction of the bookstall. Sophia sat back in her corner, with an impatient tilt of the chin.

Without the least indication of hurry or ostentation, but with that smooth, gliding motion which characterises the departure of a Great Western express, the mighty train moved almost imperceptibly forward. Even Sophia, who was on the qui vive, remained for the moment incredulous. Then she struggled to her feet with a cry of dismay, upsetting the literature in a morass on the floor of the carriage. The door was slammed upon her by a porter who might have been recruited from an institute for deaf mutes.

Sophia leant gesticulating wildly through the window. A stout Hebrew on the platform raised his hat and waved encouragingly back. In the distance Sophia caught a fleeting glimpse of Peter. He had turned from the bookstall and, standing with his back to the train, was engrossed in conversation with a lady, or woman; a lady, or woman, who left in Sophia's mind an impressionist vision of ample proportions, blonde hair and expensive furs.

The train gathered speed—

'By Jove, Margaret! Haven't seen you for years and years.'

'I hope it doesn't look years and years, Peter. What are you doing here?'

'Just come back to have a look at *Life*,' said Peter, displaying the periodical.

'Still? I should have thought you would have given up doing that now. You're a married man now.'

'All right. You're a married woman now, too.'

'Yes, I am.'

'And where's your husband, Margaret?'

'Oh, he's busy. He's in the House of Commons, you know, and he is very conscientious. Where's your wife?'

'My wife,' said Peter, turning, 'is in that—' He broke off and stared open-mouthed at a disappearing guards' van. 'Oh God!' he murmured faintly. 'My wife,' he explained, turning again to his companion, 'is somewhere between here and Bristol.'

'Bristol? That wasn't the Bristol express, was it?'

'It was.'

'What a bother! I thought – what time was it supposed to start?'

'I'm not quite sure,' replied Peter. 'But it certainly did it.'

'Bother!' repeated the lady. 'I was to have caught that train.'

'I did catch it,' said Peter. 'But I seem to have let it go again.'

# CHAPTER II

## A Stream and a Tributary

Revolution, whether of the red species advocated on the backstairs of Labour, or of the more refined but scarcely less violent kind noticeable in the drawing-rooms of the West End, is well named. It is not, as most imagine, a pulsatory movement. It is a revolutionary movement, like the movement of a wheel. It *is* the movement of a wheel. It is the movement of the wheel of Time.

For the last thirty years Mr Middling, of the Suburbs, has been sitting in the same railway carriage of his suburban line. His children will not sit in it. The railway carriage will still, no doubt, be in use, but it will be occupied by the children of the present engine-driver. Mr Middling's children will be driving the engine.

And the engine-driver's children will say, 'What a menace these fellows are.' And the guard's nephew will reply from across the carriage, 'They won't be satisfied till they've had a revolution.'

Sophia's father was a dealer in wholesale ironmongery. What with the war and what with his wife and what with one thing and another, the good, plain man found himself in more genteel circumstances at this period than had ever fallen to the lot of any of his ancestors. Then came Peter; and, briefly, the cause of Peter's variance with the wholesale ironmonger's wife was, like all such differences, attributable to the rotating wheel of Circumstance.

With centre Burlington Arcade and radius Burlington Arcade – National Sporting Club, describe a circle. The circle thus described was roughly the social circle of Peter Wykeham before his marriage. His bride's mother had no hesitation in describing it as a very vicious circle indeed;

but that was only when she discovered that Peter was diffident in inviting her inside it.

It is a circle which will be found to include all the best and several of the worst restaurants, the headquarters of all the most reliable bookmakers and every serviceable stage-door.

It also includes Berkeley Square, the Savoy and Piccadilly Hotels, Shipwright's, Thurston's and the Royal Automobile Club.

In order to marry Sophia, Peter had voluntarily enlarged his social circle; but he seems to have conveyed by suggestion to the slowly freezing mother that Sophia was the only member of the family whom he regarded in the matter. Mother very rightly resented the slightest hint of condescension. She considered that the exclusiveness of Peter's circle was due not to its distinction, but to the fact that it was an inner Babylon of prodigality and whoredom, from which every honest Kensingtonian held aloof, except on the conventional tip-and-run excursions in pursuit of shopping, tea and theatres.

If she ever found herself borne on the revolving wheel of Circumstance and landed in Berkeley Square, she was quite prepared to modify her views.

Meanwhile she certainly could not be said to pave the way for Peter's happiness. He disregarded her and she said he was a snob. For Sophia's sake he twisted his countenance into an amiable grin and tried to be hearty. Sophia's mother said he was trying to patronise her. All this time Sophia's father sat stolidly on the fence. On one occasion he accepted an invitation to lunch at Peter's club, whence he returned in so noticeable a state of exhilaration that he would have served his prospective son-in-law's interests far better had he remained and eaten his lunch upon the fence as usual.

At the marriage feast of Peter and Sophia the usual water and wine were in evidence. The water took the form of a narrow stream of semi-proscribed relations and specimens of recently arrived neighbours. Peter's friends were undeniably the wine of the party; and the best wine arrived last in the form of a small company of glorious young patricians who walked from the church and presented themselves at the tail end of the reception queue. The wine was too well-bred to display its opinion of the water, but the mixture was naturally a trifle insipid, though the water strove to augment the shortage of wine by bubbling with imitative effervescence and the conversation of novels.

But the friends of Peter, departing in a body, exchanged horrified confidences as they went their way.

'Poor old Peter!'

'What has he gone and done?'

'What a bunch!'

'Did you remark the old sort of head-squaw with beads? A great aunt of the bride, I understood.'

'Did I not. Where can she possibly have bought her hat?'

'I can only suggest Christie's. And who was Old Bill in the grey summer suiting?'

'Idiot! That was the host. The bride's father.'

'Oh, God!'

'No, not God. That was the bride's mother. I can't conceive a happier description of her.'

'What in all the Ministry of Munitions are these people?'

'Father is something in the hardware line, I am told.'

'Oh, hardware? Well, I should think he must be pretty good at his job if he produced that daughter.'

'Poor old Peter!'

It is necessary to return to the wedding in order to place on record a circumstance which was regarded as nothing more serious than a regrettable inconvenience by anybody, and by some even as a boon. Of the clergy, relatives of the bride, who had been invited to perform the marriage ceremony, one failed to arrive. They waited for him until the arrival of the bride at the church, when the service proceeded without him. It was very annoying because the announcements for the 'Marriage' columns of the morning papers had already been carefully compiled, thus:

On 2nd June, at St. Peter's, Cranley Gardens, by the
Rev. Willmott Staines, uncle of the bride, assisted by
the Rev. Andrew Cathcart Sloley Sloley-Jones, cousin of the
bride, Peter Withington Wykeham, son of the late Hugo
Wykeham, to Sophia Clarice Willmott, only child of Mr
and Mrs Ferdinand Cox Bone, of Oakley St, Chelsea.

Besides, it was very unbecoming that a girl in Sophia's position should be married by only one clergyman at a time. Her
mother was exceedingly vexed about it. But even she had to
confess that Uncle Willmott made the most of his opportunity. He addressed the young couple at great length, in-
forming Peter severely that he was the fortunate recipient of
a priceless gift. Peter, when he understood that this referred
to Sophia, resented the allusion. He had discovered that
Sophia was priceless and was surely entitled to be considered
the best judge in the matter. However, he got a little of his
own back an hour later, when he pressed Uncle's hand and
said, 'Good-bye. And many thanks for your priceless gift. We
wanted ladles.'

But where was the Rev. Andrew Cathcart Sloley Sloley-
Jones?

He had duly descended that morning in his provincial
Vicarage, clad in his wedding garment, his spectacles sparkling joyously in the morning sun. Nature could afford a gleam
of partiality for the spectacles of this enthusiastic, inquisitive, genial, annoying parson. He sounded well-con-
nected, but he was in happier circumstances than that. He
was well to do.

His housekeeper, Mrs Pugsley, unlike Nature, did not
reflect his cheerful humour. If no man is a hero to his valet,
Heaven defend the bachelor parson from his housekeeper.

'The cab had been ordered to call for you at ten,' said Mrs
Pugsley.

'The cab? Good. I had thought of cycling to the station,
but—'

'Not in those trousers,' said Mrs Pugsley.

'Beg pardon?'

'Bicycling in your best trousers before the wedding?'

'No. P'raps you're right. A cab. Right. Have we any sugar, Mrs Pugsley?'

Mrs Pugsley took about as much notice of this inquiry as the blonde behind the marble counter takes of the inferior waitress when the latter says 'Tea for one.' When she returned to the room five minutes later she brought the sugar with her, but only incidentally and along with other matters. This was Mrs Pugsley's way with sugar.

'Butt has called to see you.'

'Butt? The sanitary inspector? Queer. The man's a heathen. A hard case, Mrs Pugsley. What can he want. Delighted to see him of course, still—'

'He's come about the drains, I think.'

'The drains? Oh, but surely our drains are simply A1?'

'Any 'ow, he's standing looking at the man-hole in the front,' said Mrs Pugsley. ' 'Ere's your sugar.'

'Oh, I say, thanks. The man-hole? Righto. I'll join him in two two's.'

At the conclusion of his meal the vicar duly discovered the nether portions of his visitor protruding on to the garden path. One shoulder supported the tilted lid of the man-hole. Sloley-Jones stooped and cleared his throat. Mr Butt thereupon withdrew his head from the man-hole.

'Morning, Mr Butt. My housekeeper told me I should find you looking at the man-hole. Shall we go inside?'

'I've seen as much as I want,' replied Mr Butt, crawling to his feet. 'I didn't come 'ere to inspect you. That' – he indicated the man-hole – 'was jest by way of 'aving a busman's 'oliday, as they say. You're what they call the church clergyman of this place, aren't you?'

'Certainly. I'm the vicar of the parish church. Rather.'

'Well, if that ain't the same thing it's near enough for me,' said Mr Butt. 'And speaking for myself, and man to man and face to face' – he leant his own face slightly forward as he spoke – 'I don't 'old for religion.'

'I know. I've heard about it. Rotten state to be in, you know, Butt. Disastrous! But perhaps you've been thinking it over and want advice.'

'No,' replied Mr Butt firmly, 'I haven't and don't. But my old mother, Mrs Butt, who lives in my house in Redlands Road, was once given to it.'

'To what?'

'To religious belief.'

'Oh, good! Well?'

'And she's been sick.'

'Been sick? How rotten. What upset her do you think?'

'Been sick for years, she has.'

'Been sick for years? How awfully trying for you all.'

'It don't appear,' said Mr Butt contemplatively, 'that she can go on being sick much longer.'

'No, I should think not, poor soul,' said the vicar.

'And having been once a woman with religious thoughts, and having been sick over a number o' years, her thoughts 'ave returned to religion. Mind you, I think, meself, she's a bit weak in the head, owing to the constant sickness.'

'Well, well. Well?'

'Last night,' continued Mr Butt, dropping his voice mysteriously, 'she called me to her bedside, and I went and bent over her and she said something very low.'

'Really?' said the vicar with greater interest. 'I'm sure she didn't mean it. A trifle delirious perhaps. What did she say?'

'She spoke in a low tone.'

'Oh, I see. Yes?'

'She said she thought she was soon to go home; and she would like to see a church clergyman about the state of her condition.'

'Oh, good! I see what you mean. You want me to come and see her, poor old lady. You bet. Delighted to do anything I can.'

'Yes, now,' said Mr Butt.

'Er – yes,' said Sloley-Jones. 'I'm awfully sorry I can't come this morning, but—'

'Why not?'

'Oh, as a matter of fact I'm just off to London.'

'Ho,' said Mr Butt grimly. 'And where do you suppose my pore old mother is jest off to?'

'I'm sorry. I've got to go to a wedding. A family affair.'

'I thought your church clergyman's job in the parish was to visit the sick and needy?'

'So it is, but—'

'But instead o' coming and 'elping a pore old lady out with it, off you goes, gallivanting off to a wedding.'

'No, no. Come, I say, Butt. That's not fair. Below the belt.'

'When pore old ladies in the town and parish,' said Mr Butt, raising his voice after the manner of sanitary inspectors in argument, 'are sick and dying and suffering from pangs—'

'Below the belt, Butt,' protested Sloley-Jones.

'From pangs of conscience, or what they imagine are such, where's the church clergyman?'

'Come now, reason, reason!' said the vicar.

'Reason, a wedding,' said Mr Butt with great scorn.

His voice was now rising to a shout in a hopeful effort to swamp that of his antagonist.

'I'm sorry,' repeated Sloley-Jones. 'Can't come this morning. Imposs! Any other day.'

'Not that I care. I don't hold with religion. But what I want to know is this.'

Mr Butt's face was crimson and he shook a very dirty finger in the direction of the man-hole.

'When did you last have your drains inspected?' he cried.

'I don't know,' replied the vicar with dignity. 'They don't want inspecting, thank you. They are absolutely tip-top drains.'

'Ho! And are you aware that the local municipal authorities require every householder to be liable to fine or imprisonment if his drains are found out of order and he takes no steps to have them inspected with view to rectification?'

'I tell you—'

'And 'ave you had it done?'

Mr Butt glared at his victim with bloodshot eyes. Then, producing a worn notebook from his pocket, he turned the leaves, licking his thumb at intervals, with accompanying glances of menace at the vicar.

'I fail to see what my drains have to do with the case,' said the latter boldly. 'I know they are perfectly sweet. I should have detected the smallest flaw in my drains. Besides, you say you came here to see me about your mother. If you had been so offensively cautious about your own drains perhaps the poor old lady would not have been so dreadfully sick.'

'I know my dooty,' remarked Mr Butt, making an entry in the notebook.

The vicar shifted uneasily.

'But, Butt. Mrs Butt – your mother – will not – is not expected to pass away today, is she?'

'The longer she's sick the nearer the end,' said Mr Butt proverbially.

'It's awfully inconvenient,' murmured Sloley-Jones. 'My curate is away.'

'She asked for you,' said Mr Butt, looking up from his notebook with the air of one offering his victim a last chance.

'For me in person?'

'Yes,' said Mr Butt. 'She asked for you in person. Her mind has been wandering lately. Fer the last day and a 'alf she had been in a state bordering on absolute como.'

'But she doesn't know me personally?'

'She 'eard you speak once.'

'Oh, come. That's gratifying. When?'

'She 'eard you speak in your church. I think she went inside by reason of being caught in a thunderstorm.'

The vicar did not appear to credit this explanation. He adjusted his spectacles and glanced at his watch.

'R-redlands R-road,' he cogitated. 'I have my motor-bike.'

'Number thirteen,' said Mr Butt. 'And I don't mind reckoning this an inspection, though intended as a busman's 'oliday. I'll send a 'and to overhaul that man-hole o' yours.'

The cab waited outside the vicar's dwelling until such time as the London train was due to leave the local station, when the driver enjoyed a brief altercation with Mrs Pugsley and departed. Ten minutes later the vicar, pushing his motor-cycle and covered with dust, reappeared at his gate.

'I sent the cab away,' said Mrs Pugsley.

'Judicious,' he replied. 'But how rotten! I've missed the wedding.'

'That's the second London wedding you've missed in three weeks owing to bi-cycling about at the critical moment,' remarked Mrs Pugsley severely.

'I know. Though this was far the most important. I was going to do part of the service in this one. The other didn't matter so much. I wasn't invited even. Still, I should have liked to have gone. The bride was a Social Worker. Splendid woman! She married an M.P. too, by Jove. I should have enjoyed meeting him, Liberal as he is. But this is a much worse case, Mrs Pugsley.'

'Then you should not go bi-cycl—'

'Couldn't help it absolutely. I was ministering to the sick. I suppose I'd better go and wire to the people in London. I'd try and get there on my bicycle, but it isn't running well. In fact it isn't running at all. I think I must have got some dirt in my carburettor.'

Thus it was that towards the end of her wedding festivities, Sophia received the following belated telegram, as transcribed in the cryptography of the post office:

To Mr and Mrs Wkkeham oakley st Chelsea

   Most awfully sorry cannot participate detained Duty a Thousand regrets apologies business before pleasure but terribly disappointed sorry congratulations and All good wishes future happiness cathcart sloley-Jones.

# CHAPTER III

## Margaret

'Why are you going to Bristol?' asked Margaret.

'I'm not,' replied Peter. He spoke ruefully. Already during his brief married career he had experienced more than one sharp correction. Not that he resented this. To hear Sophia speak sharply was merely one of the less gratifying of the many varied surprises which marriage to Sophia held for him. But he had never been guilty of a lapse so serious as this confounded affair of the missed train. The situation was pregnant with misunderstanding and reproach.

'My wife is, and I ought to be, on the way to visit some people at a place called Something Fitz-Whatnot in Somerset,' he went on to explain.

'Rushcombe Fitz-Chartres?'

'Good heavens, are you Mrs Bradshaw?' cried Peter in admiration.

'The Bunters?'

'The Bunters.'

'Funny. I'm going there too.'

'How extraordinary and delightful,' said Peter. 'So we're both going to the same place – though we're not exactly plunging there at the present moment, are we? Are you friends of the Bunters then?'

'I used to stay there when I was a girl. They've asked me to bring my husband down there for the shooting.'

'Oh, yes, and to bring yourself for the ratting I gather. I notice you've got your ferret with you in your muff.'

'That is Pansy, my Schipperke pup. I couldn't leave her. Well, what are you going to do now, Peter?'

'Where's your husband?'

'Busy with his politics. I decided to go down ahead of him

because he is always so very uncertain in his movements.'

'Sounds a likely sort of a man to go shooting with,' commented Peter.

'So now I suppose I must travel down tomorrow instead. You will be doing the same thing, I take it?'

Peter did not reply for a few seconds. He was deliberating.

'It's a nuisance,' he said at length. 'You see, my wife doesn't know the Bunters from Adam and Eve – well, I don't myself if it comes to that; but I have a sort of feeling that she will be rather put out at having to spend the first night there alone without me. She never said so to me, but I think it would be a great relief to her if I could get down there this evening. I don't know why exactly, but I have a notion that she rather counts on me. I suppose it is because I have had more experience at this sort of stunt. I've got so used to meeting ladies who might quite easily be Eve that—'

'But you can't get down tonight.'

'I can if I put my mind to it,' said Peter. 'Hold on a moment now. I've got an idea. It's now one o'clock. How far is it to this place by road? I suppose two hundred miles covers it anyhow. My car's laid up, worse luck, but I know where I can hire one. Thirty into two hundred – you haven't got a piece of paper? – all right, *Life* will do. Six isn't it? Roughly six hours. Two – three— Good heavens, Margaret, I can get down there by eight o'clock, and so can you.'

'I'm game,' said Margaret with perfect calm.

'We return forthwith to my flat,' continued Peter exultantly, 'you, I, your luggage and Pansy. We eat. I telephone. The car arrives. We buzz off and get to Fitz-Thing as soon as, if not before the train. Can do?'

'Can do,' said Margaret.

'Good!' said Peter. 'As a matter of fact I was keen on doing the journey by road all along.'

A taxi was speedily summoned and Margaret's extensive luggage placed upon it.

'What will your wife do?' she asked, as Peter took his seat beside her and Pansy inside the vehicle.

'Don't ask me,' he replied. 'I'll tell you after she's done it if I survive.'

'I mean – will she go straight on to the Bunters'?'

'One cannot go straight to the Bunters' apparently, but she will find her way there of course. At least, I hope so. She's got all my gear.'

'She knows that you will follow her down immediately, which will be some consolation to her.'

'Yes, and when she sees me tonight she'll be so bucked that she'll probably let me down quite lightly after all. Oh, she's such a wonderful girl, Margaret.'

'She has to be, I expect,' said Margaret.

A few minutes later they were at Peter's flat, where refreshment was improvised by Sophia's housemaid while Peter succeeded in engaging a car by telephone. The housemaid had seen previous service in the household of Sophia's mother and was consequently influenced by strong anti-Peterite views, which were by no means mollified by his sudden return in company with a strange lady of an appearance which the housemaid decided without hesitation was worldly.

This was not the first occasion upon which Margaret's appearance had been the subject of adverse comment. Such is always the lot of a good-looking woman with expensive furs. It is quite possible that she may be blameless in character. It is a tiny fraction more possible that she is not.

And if a really striking looking woman is blameless she may ignore, but she cannot hope to remain unmolested by, the aspersions of Jealousy. And Jealousy swallows surmises as an Anglo-Indian swallows appetisers.

Margaret should never have been a Londoner. She was one of those large-limbed, healthy, cheerful women who seem more at home following a pack of hounds on a windy moorland than monopolising more than their fair share of the inadequate pavements of Bond Street. She provided a strong contrast to the other maidens there; hence perhaps the fascination which she seemed to exercise over men; hence Jealousy; hence, in due course, a scandal.

It was not a very serious scandal. Something connected with a married artist and a notorious studio-flat. But it sufficed. Margaret, dignified still, but maligned and deeply mortified, shook herself free and plunged into good works at charitable institutions. Margaret should never have been a Londoner. In the country you can be kind to any poor, disreputable Lothario and get away with it.

The men redoubled their attentions. Some of them loved her despite it all. Some of them loved her all the more because of it all. Some of the younger ones had mothers and allowances, but were prepared to go to Australia with her.

Margaret, however, shrouded herself in a veil of reserve and retirement. She seldom obstructed Bond Street now. She was usually to be found at an orphanage at Walthamstow or a crèche at Islington. She saw few of her old friends. And few of her old friends saw her. Jealousy triumphant retired.

Then came the announcement that Margaret was to marry Mr Claude Hackett, M.P. The tidings surprised everybody. An undistinguished Wee Free member for a secluded Eastern County constituency – why, a provincial mayor's daughter might have thought twice about him! Who was he anyway? A young man of the highest ambition and a modest fortune acquired rapidly in the Far East.

'My hat!' said Peter, when he heard. 'Poor old Margaret, who might have chosen the reddest rosebud in the garden, has been driven to settle down on what sounds like a good-looking cauliflower. See what comes of turning into a chrysalis just because somebody calls you a butterfly and you don't like it, my boy.'

The boy addressed murmured some conventionality. He didn't seem as interested in the subject as Peter was.

'Oh, it's all very well for you to say she has made her bed and must lie on it,' proceeded Peter. 'Why should she lie alongside a husband like that? I haven't met him but he sounds extraordinarily dour and I bet you he's as good a Methodist as was ever Prussian to a fallen housemaid.'

'Why doesn't Peter marry the girl himself, if he makes such a song about her?' Thus club gossip backbites. 'Instead of striking out that line of his own in artistic ironmongery?'

Enough. Both Peter and Margaret were duly married in accordance with their own tastes in the matter. Both appeared entirely satisfied and both received at the time telegrams of congratulation from each other, from Lady Bunter and from the Rev. Cathcart Sloley Sloley-Jones.

Margaret's mother, who was a mere incarnated scent-bottle at Bath, had long since ceased to count. That dear old, inconspicuous, reliable friend of a former generation, Lady Bunter of Rushcombe Fitz-Chartres, was of more practical value. She had never for one moment credited the horrid stories that had been circulated. Margaret careless with a married artist? Unthinkable! Lady Bunter had had Margaret down to stay with her at the time when the trouble originated. And, now that she was happily married, she must bring her nice M.P. husband down for the shooting.

The well-appointed limousine from Gamble's garage drew up outside the block of flats. The driver, who was a large man with a red moustache, carefully selected and pressed Peter's bell. This brought the house-parlourmaid, who asked the red man sharply what he wanted.

'Car ordered here for a long trip – name o' Wykeham. That's right, ain't it?' he explained according to his wont.

The housemaid took a frowning survey of the car and stiffened visibly.

'When were you sent for?' she asked.

'Ordered by phone from Gamble's garridge not a matter of a quarter of a hour back. A long trip I was told. Right away somewhere. Will that luggage be for me, miss?'

He indicated the extensive pile of heterogeneous baggage

affected by Margaret, which had been deposited in the hall of the building.

'I don't doubt,' said the maid trenchantly, following his glance.

The driver entered the hall and took stock.

'Would this be a 'oneymoon outfit?' he inquired slyly.

'Certainly not,' said the maid.

'Ah,' proceeded the driver with interest, commencing his operations by placing one box on the top of another, removing it again and selecting the nethermost. 'I generally knows by the look of the outfit. For such as is interested in such studies luggage is full of interest. 'Oneymoon, I thought, 'ere. Not long married, miss, you grant me?'

The housemaid stiffened again and shook her head.

'Though none of your business,' she replied, 'the couple is not a married couple.'

The driver paused in his action of raising the first box, turned his head and whistled.

'Not living in sin?' he suggested faintly.

'How dare you say such things to me?' said the housemaid.

'Don't take it amiss. They aren't the only ones.'

'That'll do from you,' said the housemaid.

She shook indignant shoulders. The driver resumed operations with the box. He jerked it into the required position and remarked:

'I throw no stones.'

'I don't wish to hear from you again,' was the reply. 'You get about your business.'

The driver complied with a final and somewhat vague statement of his willingness to take the rough with the smooth, which he seemed to consider disposed of the matter amicably. Peter, Margaret and Pansy then put in an appearance.

'I don't seem to know you,' said Peter, as the process of loading was completed. 'I thought I knew all the men from Gamble's. What's your name?'

'Dann,' said the driver.

'Dann. And can you shift pretty rapidly if put to it, Dann?'

'Infringement risks yours, sir?'

'Of course.'

Dann stole a furtive glance at Peter and scratched his red moustache.

'And I take it I don't altogether fade from the mem'ry when I've got you there?' he asked.

'I wish Gamble's had sent one of the men who know me,' was Peter's comment.

'Right, sir; that's all right,' said Dann hastily. 'I can take any o' them on any time. I was a Air Force motor-cyclist at one time, I was.'

'Were you though! Well, look here. Hounslow – Bath – stop when you get to Glastonbury, and I'll ask the rest of the way.'

Dann made no verbal assent. He merely expectorated and grasped the gear lever. His red moustache bristled with zeal. Peter smiled faintly and climbed in.

'I shouldn't be surprised if we get down to the Bunters' for tea,' he said.

# CHAPTER IV

## The Nest

The village of Maiden Blotton was as miniature and as isolated as any to be found on the Somerset countryside, and remains so today. There are a few desultory houses in the neighbourhood, and it was, no doubt, on behalf of the occupants of these houses that the quaint little church with the high pews was originally erected away there in the fields, for even country folks require continual admonition of the soul and ultimately a hallowed acre for the body. But there was not a Vicarage at Maiden Blotton, the admonition referred to being the secondary Sabbath consideration of a hard-riding parson from Downblotton, five miles away. Yet Maiden Blotton ranked as a place, being openly advertised as such to the high road traveller, though, so far as can be ascertained, that inscription on the cracked signpost along the Glastonbury road – 'Maiden Bloton 2¼m.' – constitutes the only written record of her existence in the whole of geography.

Maiden Blotton or Bloton (the phonetics of the signwriter are unreliable) possessed one redeeming feature. The church, standing in damp estrangement, with the churchyard walls worn and crumbled into gaps through which moody cows were wont to stray in order to scratch their backs on the grateful Bathstone of the monuments; the three or four cottages across the road, painted black for economy and inhabited by rustics connected with the maintenance of the cattle aforesaid, or, less vivaciously, of turnips – these alone would barely have justified the signpost. But fifty yards down the road, linked to the cottages by a prosperous plantation of crab-apple trees, stood an inn – and Maiden Blotton was a place.

It was an inn with a double frontage of bar and parlour respectively, easily distinguishable from without by the degrees of refinement in window inscriptions; the parlour being labelled 'ales', and the bar 'beers'. Of the fact that stabling could also be provided no advertisement was necessary.

At about 7.30 on the evening of the eighteenth of September, the landlady of this inn came through the open doorway into the road to perform the regular evening ritual known to her as 'taking a last look round'. This consisted of stepping into the middle of the road, literally looking round her in all directions and returning again to the inn, the door of which was then closed and further custom neither invited nor esteemed. This practice had originated in the days when the landlady's late husband conducted the affairs of the inn; though his last look round had usually taken the form of a final and opportune breath of fresh air before he went, or was put, to bed. Since his wife's accession the last look merely served to inform any of the gentlemen interested in turnips further up the road that if they intended to patronise the bar that evening they would have to run; and was in this respect a totally futile measure; all the gentlemen in question having invariably found their way to the inn a good half-hour before.

This evening the landlady took her last look round somewhat hurriedly, for there was the chill of approaching autumn in the air and on each side of the road the mists were settling upon an almost unbroken horizon of turnips. There were already lights in the windows of the inn, and the signboard which stretched between those of the first floor, setting forth the announcement 'The Stag and Hunt by A. Spoker. Beers. Beers', was scarcely legible in the waning light.

Mrs Spoker glanced with satisfaction at the lights in the windows as she retraced her steps into the inn. Her bedroom accommodation usually more than sufficed her; claims to that extent upon the hospitality of the *Stag and Hunt* were few. At the moment, for a change, both the bedrooms available for visitors were occupied. The room above the bar was assigned to an old lady who, it seemed, having suddenly become bedridden, had had the misfortune to be at Maiden Blotton when this calamity had occurred and, lacking friends and relatives, promised to remain ridden above the bar till further notice. The room over the parlour was being patronised by Mr and Mrs Love, owners of one of those desultory houses in the neighbourhood, at which house repairs, which apparently amounted practically to demolition, had driven them temporarily to the inn.

Mrs Spoker, who was a long, bony woman with high shoulders and a moustache, indulged a severe self complacency at these unwonted circumstances. This took the form of a voluntary statement, to everyone with whom she came in contact, in these terms – 'I am completely occupied.' This Mrs Spoker regarded as a polite interpretation of the more vulgar 'I am full up,' a phrase which she could not in her mind disconnect with certain deplorable episodes in the curtailed career of that A. Spoker commemorated by the signboard. And, since Mrs Spoker found no occasion to employ this satisfactory report of her condition as a pretext or apology, its frequent reiteration must have been a modest boast which was undoubtedly justified by the exceptional nature of her occupation.

Even so, it was strange to hear Mrs Spoker boast; for she was a woman of the most rigid and inexorable principles. Irreligious thought and worldly motive were to her as the defilement which she shook from her duster, as with averted head and disgusted expression she stood for a few vigorous morning moments in the open window of her parlour. By some paradoxical evolution rancour and intolerance have been established in the vanguard of primitive Christianity. Mrs Spoker, in common with many of the stricter disciples of righteousness, was as inclement in demeanour as she was cadaverous in aspect.

Mrs Spoker closed the inn door and retired into an

artificial room, which had been constructed by partitioning off a corner of the hall. This served as the reception office and possessed the regulation glass shutter through which intending patrons could be inspected, an album for purposes of registration, a keyrack, the landlady's account books and cashbox, a Christmas calendar for the year before last and various other of the recognised conventions of such a chamber. It spoke highly for the cleanliness which was next to godliness in Mrs Spoker that the dust of disuse had never been allowed to settle upon any of these articles; but even her watchfulness had been unable to prevent the frame of the glass shutter from warping in such a manner that it was now impossible to raise it; with the result that, on the rare occasions when an intending visitor appeared, the latter was first treated to a display of dumbshow by Mrs Spoker from within and afterwards forced to enter the office in order to sign the register which remained heavily chained to its counter.

The shutter, being thus permanently closed, excluded sound from outside. Mrs Spoker remained unaware of footsteps and a conversation in the road before the inn door, and sat surveying her accounts by the light of a candle with that concentration of her thick eyebrows which is characteristic of moral rectitude intent on getting its money's worth.

'Ha!' cried Peter, releasing one of the smaller but by no means the lightest of Margaret's valises and gazing intently upwards to discern the legend between the windows. 'I told you there was bound to be a pub at Maiden Bloton. Here you are – "The Stag and Hunt by A. Spoker. Beers. Beers." Doesn't that warm your heart?'

'It's more than two and a quarter miles,' said Margaret with some ingratitude.

'Never mind, we're here,' said Peter. He indicated the bar window as he spoke. 'Beers, again. This is really most encouraging. Beers! There's something peculiarly alluring in the use of that plural. I feel sure we have found our haven at last, Margaret.'

'Well, what about going into it?' said Margaret.

She opened the door, and Peter, who still carried one bag, again raised the other and followed her into the inn. The hall was illumined only by the light of Mrs Spoker's candle shining through the glass shutter.

'At last!' repeated Peter, dropping Margaret's luggage in the hall with a sigh of relief. 'What a fatigue! Are you dead, Margaret?'

'I am tired rather, I'm afraid.'

'Hungry?'

'Yes. Are you?'

'Am I? If I hadn't felt so confident that there must be a pub at a place with a name like Maiden Bloton I should have devoured Pansy on the way here. Anyhow, all is well now. We'll get some dinner of sorts here and a couple of bedrooms of sorts and some breakfast of sorts, by which time Dann will arrive, and then Bunter ho!'

There was little of Peter's usual exhilaration in this optimism. Even his spirits had dropped beneath the ordeal of carrying two heavy bags for miles along an otherwise deserted road in the twilight of an unreasonably dark September evening. Margaret's gentle complacency had suffered still more perceptibly. To engage voluntarily in a cross-country walk is a very different proposition to being suddenly evicted from a car which develops a violent leak in the radiator in a locality which appears to be first cousin to a prairie, and being forced to tramp dejectedly in search of shelter for the approaching night. Conversation on the road, at first speculatively merry, had gradually hardened in tone. Margaret had more than once expressed her desire to return to the car; Peter had insisted on his visionary inn at Maiden Bloton. And even now beneath the promising sign of the *Stag and Hunt*, with the smell of cooking mingling curiously with the permanent evidence of the stabling, Margaret felt that it required an effort beyond her present capabilities to accord Peter his due. She contented herself with sitting uncomfortably on one of the bags, as the only alternative to standing for a moment longer, and with saying with as much equanimity as she could muster:

'Well, do please let us get the rooms and order the dinner, shall we?'

'Rather,' said Peter. He moved forward and looked through the glass shutter. 'That's right. This is evidently the bureau,' he reported.

'Is there anyone there?'

'Yes, a rather curious looking man in a blouse.'

'Knock him up,' said Margaret, suppressing a yawn.

The surprise in Mrs Spoker's face gave way to a hard smile of pleasure as she scented the possibilities of this stranger. If to be completely occupied was gratifying, the opportunity of turning a solicitous wanderer from her door was an almost undreamt-of luxury. For some moments she and Peter engaged in mutual gesticulation through the glass.

'Pull that shutter thing up and talk to him,' urged Margaret.

'The damn thing's stuck,' said Peter, 'and I can't talk to him for two reasons. In the first place it's not him at all, it's a woman; and in the second place she's deaf and dumb.'

'Then go in and write things,' said Margaret.

Peter was about to comply when Mrs Spoker appeared from the door of the office bearing her candle, by the light of which she inspected her visitors with a hopeful scowl.

'Good evening. We want two—' Margaret began.

'I am completely occupied,' said Mrs Spoker.

'Oh, I'm so sorry; I thought you looked busy,' said Peter. 'But, you see we had to let you know we'd got here, didn't we? We've had a misfortune with our car and we shall have to dine and sleep here tonight.'

'Where are you going to sleep?' asked Mrs Spoker.

'Well, I suppose you know where your bedrooms are better than I do,' said Peter.

'I tell you,' repeated Mrs Spoker. 'I'm completely occupied.'

'Oh, you mean you're full up?' cried Peter, his jaw dropping.

'Completely occupied,' said Mrs Spoker.

Peter met Margaret's eye and winced.

'But can't we get put up anywhere here?' he asked desperately.

Mrs Spoker shook her head and gave vent to a long whistling negative.

'Oh, hell!' whispered Peter to himself, but not too softly to evade the ears of Mrs Spoker who frowned deeply. 'We can get some dinner here anyhow, I suppose?' he continued.

'Not if you blarspheme,' said Mrs Spoker.

'I'm sorry,' said Peter. 'I didn't mean you to hear it.'

'The Almighty heard it,' said Mrs Spoker.

'How do you know?' said Peter with growing irritation.

Mrs Spoker turned severely to Margaret.

'You should know better than to allow him to blarspheme in my 'otel,' she observed.

'I do,' answered Margaret, who noted the necessity for conciliation. 'I didn't hear him or I would have stopped him.'

Mrs Spoker shook her head.

'The vile word is spoke by that time and soon forgot most like. But the entry is made against him in the book from which there is no rubbing out,' was her pessimistic comment.

'Can we have some dinner?' asked Margaret.

Mrs Spoker drew herself up and gave vent to a prolonged hiss like a doubtful serpent.

'I am not at all sure that you can have any dinner neither,' she temporised. 'We're very strict 'ere. This is my 'otel, and into it I admit only such as meets with my own approval.'

'I'm surprised to hear you're full up,' said Peter.

Both ladies treated him to frowns.

'We're very tired and hungry,' said Margaret in imploring tones, 'and we've still to find a night's shelter.'

'By the way, is there a telephone here?' asked Peter.

'No,' snapped Mrs Spoker.

'Where's the nearest town?'

'Downblotton, five miles on,' said Mrs Spoker.

'Five miles, good Lord!'

'What was that?'

'I said "five miles with a good load." It's a long way. Have you a cab or a cart of anything of the sort?'

'No.'

'Well, is there one to be got in the place?'

'What place?'

'Why, this conf – confraternity – this village.'

'No.'

'My God – h'm – my godmother lives not far away,' said Peter. 'If I could only find some means of communicating with her.'

Mrs Spoker, who saw through this, contented herself with a cold shiver of the shoulders. For some moments nothing further was said. Finally Margaret tried again.

'When can we have some dinner?' she asked.

Mrs Spoker turned and watched her for a few seconds, as though deliberating whether the appearance of the lady visitor compensated for the evident godlessness of her companion to the extent of justifying a meal at the exacting *Stag and Hunt*. At length, raising her rasping voice, Mrs Spoker called:

'Gladys.'

'It's as well for you, madam,' she went on, 'that you take no part in your 'usband's ways: and as well for him also. He would get no dinner from me else. Blarsphemy, I ab'or.'

'Look here, this lady is not—' Peter stopped short, as he noticed Margaret shaking her head with an animated frown in his direction.

'Is not what?' asked Mrs Spoker.

'Is not able to do any more walking tonight. Are you sure you can't put her up?'

Before Mrs Spoker replied the parlour door opened and a miniature domestic appeared. The landlady turned upon her as though she had surprised her in the action of robbing the till.

'Gladys, why 'ave you not lit the 'all lamp? Bring it immediate.'

The foolish virgin thus admonished was about to comply, when she was again accosted.

'And there will be another two dinners when Mr and Mrs Love 'as finished.'

Gladys's only comment was a sigh – a form of expression to which she was justifiably prone, and which, in co-operation with chronic adenoids, was not easily distinguishable from an habitual grunt. As she proceeded to the rear of the hall to obtain the lamp, Mrs Spoker returned to the subject of her rooms with some avidity.

'Both my bedrooms are completely occupied,' she repeated. 'If it were not so, seeing the circumstances, I might offer you one of them.'

'And there is not another pub – lic hotel, or even a cottage, where we could—'

'Cottage?' cried Mrs Spoker. 'In the cottages here they sleeps so unhealthy already that I wouldn't ask a dog to share 'em – not a dog, no, nor yet a cat, Seven and eight in a room – immoral in my way of thinking.'

'You're quite right,' said Peter pacifically. 'It ought to be stopped. I never heard of such an orgy. I shouldn't dream of trying to get a bed there under those circumstances.'

'Nor you wouldn't if you wanted,' said Mrs Spoker.

At this point Gladys reappeared with a large oil lamp, which, by stretching to the very limit of her reach, she managed to balance precariously on a wall bracket in the hall. The effort called for such a rapid and strident succession of grunts that even Pansy, who had hitherto remained asleep in Margaret's muff, commenced to display symptoms of uneasiness. No sooner, however, had Gladys performed her dangerous task and retired again into the parlour, than another individual appeared with a sudden, rather tentative movement from the road.

This was a swarthy young man of local farming type with a red face, a shifty eye, and ex-army breeches. As soon as he noticed Mrs Spoker he made as though to retire into the road, but the landlady was on him in a flash.

'Out with you,' she cried. 'I'll have none of you here, as you should know by this time.'

The young man hesitated in the doorway and turned his shifty eyes inquisitively towards Margaret.

'Aa – aa oonly called in fur to see 'Arry 'Ook who's inside o' thet bar o' yours, Missus Spooker,' he murmured.

'Out with you,' repeated the landlady, making waving motions in his face with her fingers. 'I'll have none of you corrupting of my 'otel nor of Harry 'Ook neither, which is a respectable married man. Out you go.'

The abashed farmer allowed himself a last, lingering glance at Margaret and retreated into the road with a submission which was astonishing in one so robust. Mrs Spoker closed the door after him with a bang and turned in triumph to her visitors.

'There you see,' she cried. 'If I chooses not to 'ave any undesirable person in my 'otel, out they goes.'

'What's the matter with him?' asked Margaret wearily.

'Matter? 'E'es a sinner, that's what the matter is with him,' said Mrs Spoker comprehensively. ' 'E goes about with young women.'

The idea that the undesirable patron might have been able to render assistance spurred Peter to ill-advised protest.

'But surely it is not a crime for a man to go about with young women?' he said with the smile of a curate in controversy.

'It is here,' was the brief reply.

'His intentions may be honourable.'

'His aren't,' said Mrs Spoker.

Peter sighed.

'I don't see how they are ever going to get to know each other,' he remarked.

Margaret was frowning again.

Mrs Spoker drew herself up for a crushing rejoinder.

'That man,' she declared emphatically, indicating the inn door with a quivering forefinger, 'the first time as 'e ever came to this 'otel, 'e asks for accommodation, which I, not knowing him, and not being at the time completely occupied, gives 'im. 'E was travelling with a young woman, 'is wife 'e gives it out, just as to all intense and purposes you and your wife has arrived here this evening. But was she 'is wife? No, she was not 'is. She was the wife of another, and there 'e was taking 'er about the country as though they was united into 'oly wedlock according to the sight of God.'

'Perhaps they didn't occupy the same room,' suggested Peter, with a fugitive glance at Margaret.

Mrs Spoker laughed such a suggestion away bitterly.

'It is not a nice subject,' she said. 'Nor was it till a week later that I discovered the truth. And whatever rooms they occupied, do you think I should 'ave took 'em in here, and they travelling the country together, and she with her husband, a commercial up in the Midlands and in ignorance of they so doing?'

'I see,' said Peter. 'So that the fact that they were travelling together—'

'Is enough for me,' said Mrs Spoker. 'Do you think I don't know what such is up to? It is not a nice subject, especially before your wife. But I'm just a-showing you what happens to persons who comes here when I don't consider them desirable.'

Peter turned slowly to Margaret with a thoughtful tilt of his eyebrows. Mrs Spoker followed his movement with a gleam of dawning suspicion on her stern face. From Peter her glance travelled with deadly swiftness to Margaret. The latter was regarding her with a complacent smile of patient innocence.

'Do you think that Mr and Mrs Love will have finished their dinner soon?' she asked.

# CHAPTER V

## 'Sing Cuccu Nu'

Having completed the first course, which was soup, Margaret looked up almost shamefacedly from her plate. All the brightness had returned to her expression. She laid her hand gently on Peter's sleeve.

'Forgive me if I was irritable, Peter. I did want my food.'

'My dear Margaret – irritable nothing, as they say in Congress. In the first place you weren't irritable; and, in the second, if you were so fiendishly hungry as to want this soup you must have put up a truly wonderful show of patience. No, it was I who nearly put the hat on it.'

'Never so nearly as when you were on the point of saying that I wasn't really your wife. If she knew the truth we shouldn't have been allowed in the stables.'

'And now I wonder what the dickens we had better do about sleeping,' said Peter. 'You see, even if we go on, Dann won't find us in the morning.'

'Yes, but on the other hand, if we could get on to the next town, we might be able to telephone to the Bunters.'

'Five miles! My dear Margaret, you are certainly a wonderful advertisement for this soup and a very weak whisky and soda.'

This was true. From the weary traveller, sinking in the last stages of fatigue on to her baggage in the hall, Margaret was already transformed to a strong and vigorous young woman with a high colour and a gay enthusiasm for their minor adventure. She was very human. Had she not found cause to drill herself to studied reticence of recent years she might perhaps have been an emotional woman. She gave this impression now, as, alone with Peter, she allowed full play to that careless animation which follows hunger appeased. The most rapid and the most seductive transition in all human nature is that which attends the palliation of a ravenous appetite. There is something humiliating about it. Can you, who lay down your fork or your tankard with a purr of urbane satisfaction, be he who, but a few moments ago, was cursing a willing waiter for refusing to alter all the laws of Thermology in the cooking of your steak? Can those harmless but refined fellow-diners be the selfish cads whose gluttony and personal appearance so raised your contemptuous wrath on your arrival? Were you not childishly hasty in projecting an assault upon one of the younger of them for smiling when you shouted at the waiter? Ah, it is not the least cause for condemnation in Judas Iscariot that the greatest crime in history was committed at the conclusion and not in the dire necessity of a meal.

Having done full justice to the soup, they discussed the prospect cheerfully. Already the clouds were rapidly dispersing. There remained an interval of three long hours between them and normal bedtime. Tomorrow, at all events, they would make Rushcombe Fitz-Chartres. If they had to remain awake until then, they had often done the same thing at a dance. And this was just as much fun as a good many of the dances they had known. After all, they were in England. Why had they allowed their spirits to behave as though the leak in the radiator had suddenly been sprung upon them in the heart of the Caucasus? And so on.

Then Margaret turned to Peter quickly, as though struck by a thought.

'Peter, how selfish I've been. I've nothing to worry about. You have.'

'What?'

'Your wife.'

Peter laughed.

'That sounds like a good old back-hander for Sophia,' he said.

'Don't be foolish. You know what I mean. You were so keen on getting down so as not to disappoint her. And now—'

Peter raised his eyes thoughtfully to hers. There was a faint suggestion of restrained humour in his expression.

'It's a very dangerous subject here, Margaret. If the old lady heard us discussing my wife she would countermand the next course, which I judge from sounds of labour in the passage to be imminent.'

He was right. Gladys entered at that moment with hash, which she placed before them with clumsy haste and abandoned with a snort of relief.

'Anyhow,' said Margaret, 'I shall be able to assure your wife that noble sentiments inspired you to take Dann.'

'Careful,' said Peter. 'I think Gladys has only gone for veg.'

'She gives due notice of her coming,' said Margaret.

Peter was silent. The reference to Sophia seemed to have dispirited him. Margaret smiled at him gently with her kind eyes.

'Tell me, Peter,' she said quietly, 'just between you and me and Andrew Usher, how does married life strike you?'

Peter stroked his hair, deliberating.

'I think it's awfully purifying,' he said slowly. 'It makes you realise that half the ideas and aims in life which you considered great are really frightfully punk when analysed. Marriage analyses. Within three months I've discovered that a great many of the instincts and things which I thought gold are in reality the other muck – alloy or whatever it's called. Aren't I poetical?'

'Very,' said Margaret.

'I think Sophia has a stronger will than I have. If I'd known that I was going to have to do some of the things I have to do now, I wouldn't have got married; and yet I find I do the things now not because I have to do them but because I want to do them. Do you get me?'

'No married person could help getting you, Peter.'

'I thought when I got married that I was going to do what I liked. Instead of that, I find it's exactly the other way round. I like what I do.'

'And does she like it?'

'She ought to. She thinks of it. I don't suppose that Sophia is the sort of girl who shows her feelings much. Now you are, Margaret. Anyone can see that you're happy. It's simply written in your face these days.'

'Thank you, you dear,' said Margaret with genuine pleasure.

'I hope Sophia's happy,' he went on more pensively.

Margaret gave him a little intimate smile of approval.

'Go on really hoping that, Peter, and you needn't worry one little scrap about all the doing of all the things in the world.'

'Beware,' said Peter. 'Hunting noises without. Enter Gladys with veg.'

They entered upon the second course with undiminished relish, Pansy participating.

Presently, however, Margaret paused and sat upright with her chin raised, listening. Simultaneously Peter performed an exactly similar action. Their eyes met.

'Horse!' said Margaret.

'And cart!' said Peter.

They were on their feet in an instant. Margaret stepped to the window.

'Quick, Peter! Run and stop it.'

'I will, if it doesn't stop of its own accord.'

'Don't risk it. It's coming nearer. It doesn't seem to be pulling up. Peter, you must stop it, by hook or by crook.'

'Righto,' said Peter, eyeing the doorway reluctantly, 'but I hope it will save me the trouble. I wonder whether the driver knows about the beers – beers. I must say I rather hate the idea of running and trying to stop a horse by hook.'

'Now!' cried Margaret from the window. 'Quickly! Oh, all right; it's stopping.'

'Thank heaven!' said Peter.

'It's a waggonette – going our way,' reported Margaret, shading her eyes. 'Peter, I think we're saved.'

She returned briskly to Peter's side.

'All that remains,' she said, 'is for you to go and be awfully tactful. You will be better without me. I expect it is a job which will best be done in the bar.'

The driver of the waggonette had already entered the hall. He was a thin, pink man of the type indubitably connected with stables. He seemed familiar with the formalities of the *Stag and Hunt*, for he merely rapped on the glass shutter with his knuckles and summoned Mrs Spoker with a jerk of his head. They conversed in an awe-struck undertone at the office door.

'I'll tell them,' said the landlady at length, moving rapidly towards the staircase. 'You bide here. None o' that bar now. You may be required hurried.'

She mounted the stairs and a moment later could be heard knocking at the door of the bedroom above the parlour.

Peter stepped from the shadows of the parlour threshold into the hall. Within a minute he returned, nodded encouragingly to Margaret, and mixed a whisky and water. His next stay in the hall was of longer duration.

Margaret was more than once on the point of following him, but refrained, wisely conceiving that the rescuer might prove less amenable if confronted by his supernumaries *en masse*. The sight of Peter's face when he again entered the parlour was ample reward for her patience.

'Well done, Peter,' she exclaimed, without waiting for his report.

'My dear, it's better than that,' he answered. 'The most wonderful stroke of fortune!' He replaced the glass on the table and seated himself in a leisurely manner. 'There's no panic. I'll ring for the pudding,' he added.

'The stage thunder' – Peter pointed upwards to the ceiling, whence, indeed, proceeded a series of rumbling noises, punctuated by an occasional bang – 'is caused by the Loves packing.'

'Packing?'

'Packing in hot haste. Our friend the cart has come to fetch 'em away, fetch 'em away, fetch 'em away—'

'Where to?'

'Home. They are local people. Their home is being "done up", as they say. They must be rather foolhardy to leave their house and all that it contains to be crashed by navvies, but they did. One of the things they left was a genuine antique woman, Mrs Love's mother.'

'Well? Surely she hasn't been crashed by navvies?'

'That is precisely what has occurred,' said Peter dramatically. 'It doesn't take much to make a navvy put anything down, and our guardian angel had no difficulty in persuading one of the navvies to put down his bucket. His reason, it seems, was that he had to put down his bucket because he was going to think about a ladder. Anyhow, at that moment Mrs Love's mother comes round the corner, avoids the ladder for luck, and takes a prize toss over the bucket. Oh, isn't it perfectly splendid?'

'But why?'

'Why? My dear Margaret, the old lady is eighty odd. You can't go cartwheeling about over buckets at that age. Even in the profession you'll generally find that anything over sixty simply holds the handkerchief and rests on her laurels. The Loves are not a troupe, though they sound like one, and the old lady rested with great force upon her hip. She is now in bed with the doctor— I'm not talking scandal; the driver is my authority. They seem to be people of queer habits altogether. The driver eventually had to leave me because Mr Love put his head over the staircase and told him with some heat to go upstairs and help him lash his wife's trunk. Rather waste of time, I thought, even if a relief to the feelings.'

'But I really don't see how all this affects us, Peter.'

'Why, what more do you want? In about three minutes the room upstairs will be completely unoccupied.'

'Oh, I see. But that's only one room, Peter.'

'I don't want a room. I'll encamp in this parlour or anywhere. The point is we can get fixed up without having to slog along to the next village.'

'But won't it be very uncomfortable for you?'

'Not a bit. It's a magnificent solution. Directly the tumult and the shouting dies we will interview the landlady and—'

He paused. They interchanged a significant glance.

'Yes, we shall have to go rather warily with that landlady,' said Margaret with a short laugh.

Peter rose and peered into the passage.

'There seems to be no response to that pudding bell,' he remarked. 'I think we'll leave it, shall we?'

'Yes, I've had quite enough. But look here, Peter. About this business. If we tell that woman that we're not married—'

'She'll out us without a moment's hesitation. Fancy if all hotels were so strict. Brighton front would be one large dormitory.'

'It makes it a little bit awkward,' said Margaret dubiously.

'We might pretend to be brother and sister.'

'Oh, nonsense! We've already given her to understand that we're married.'

'Well, that's all right, Margaret,' said Peter, a little self-consciously.

'It's not all right. If we take the bedroom why should you sleep in the parlour?'

'My dear Margaret, of course we know that it would be all right, but while people continued to cherish such nasty minds I think it would be better for me to sleep in the parlour.'

'Oh, don't be silly, Peter. What I am asking you is – what will the landlady think of the husband who sleeps in the parlour?'

'Ah, I follow your meaning with reluctance,' said Peter. 'Well, I don't see why the landlady should know anything about it. We can book the room and climb up to it together with candles, like any old, fed-up married couple. When the house is quiet I'll sneak back here. You needn't start to undress till I go.'

'I should hope not,' said Margaret.

'I don't see why you should hope not in that strain,' protested Peter. 'I thought it was rather a brilliant idea.'

'What about the morning?'

'In the morning I sneak out again and moon about till you come down. The whole thing is perfectly simple.'

Margaret hesitated, her fingers playing restlessly with a locket at her breast. In her placid eyes was the reflection of painful memories. She seemed to drive them away with sudden resolution.

'Yes,' she said. 'It's the only thing to be done. We simply daren't risk a confession to the landlady after what she said. She may be difficult enough to manage as it is. And, after all, we needn't tell anyone that we even pretended to be married. Anyone outside the inn, I mean.'

'No, I won't lie awake composing a song about it for Sophia,' said Peter.

Margaret was about to deprecate this attitude and to prepare a list of possible participants of the secret, commencing with Claude and Lady Bunter, when the conversation was interrupted by a medley descriptive of domestic traffic from outside the parlour. The boots of heavily laden men began to beat an uncertain tattoo on the stairs. Dislocated stair-rods twanged ominously. The sharp tenor of Mr Love and the pessimistic bass of the driver engaged in what appeared to be a laborious anthem, swelling during the descent into a crescendo of 'Go on, go on. – Steady, oh, steady, sir. – Go on, I say. – Oh, steady a moment. – Go on, I say, go on.' Female voices, raised in lamentation and instruction from the landing above, blended effectively; while the fact that Gladys had been commissioned to partake in one of the more strenuous of the tasks connected with the move was suggested by an intermittent sound not unlike that produced by the low notes of a flute.

From the parlour door Margaret and Peter watched the procession with thoughtful interest. Mr Love and the driver carried between them their former perquisite, the trunk of Mrs Love. Behind them a smaller but substantial piece of luggage was borne by Gladys and an aged male retainer, seconded from duties in the bar. That both Mrs Spoker and

Mrs Love, in the rear, were heavily laden with minor im-
pedimenta gave the watchers reason to hope that the evacu-
ation was to be complete and final.

The departure was not unduly prolonged. In the road Mr
Love and the driver favoured the company with a brief
chanty running 'Got it? – No, I ain't, 'old on. – Got it? Got
it? – No, 'old on sir.' Within the door Mrs Spoker hastily
imparted to Mrs Love a few final sentiments on the subject
of Divine Intention in the disposition of buckets; farewells
and last commiserations; a deep, guttural instigation to the
horse; and the wheels of the waggonette crunched heavily
away into obscurity.

'I think you'd better tackle her,' said Peter.

Margaret, refreshed, certainly had a persuasive charm
about her. Mrs Spoker was duly lured into the parlour on her
way back from speeding the Loves, was spoken fair and
thanked for the excellence of her dinner, Peter remaining
diplomatically in the background. Margaret exercised the
most admirable discretion. She listened with an impressed
air to a home-made parable concerning the elder Mrs Love
and the bucket. Beneath her softening influence Mrs Spoker
became quite human. She agreed almost cordially to allow
Margaret the use of the bedroom. Having done so, however,
she seemed momentarily to regret the decision, as her dark-
ening frown rested on Peter. She turned again to Margaret
and inquired in a transparently false tone of conversation
how long she had been married. Three months, Margaret
told her with innocent promptitude. Mrs Spoker nodded
grimly.

'Very well,' she said. 'I will see to the girl making the bed
up.'

In the doorway she halted and directed another somewhat
inimical glance at Peter.

'You will have to sign the book,' she told him, as though
pronouncing an ultimatum.

'Certainly,' said Peter, with creditable coolness.

'And – what is the name?'

'May I come in?' said a voice – a high-pitched effusive, male voice.

Mrs Spoker turned sharply and threw open the door.

'Oh, thank you. I – I hope I don't intrude,' said the owner of the voice, entering the parlour.

He was a clerical gentleman of about thirty-eight. There was something exasperatingly dry about his appearance. His clothes were very dusty and he had a habit of working his mouth open and shut as though his throat were dusty too. Round the ends of his trousers were khaki leggings of the type affected by marines. His hands and the cuffs of his shirt were sadly dirty. In one hand he held a spanner, not aggressively but as one would hold a pencil. In contrast, however, to his deplorable condition his manner seemed philosophically hearty; and his eyes, magnified by large gold-rimmed spectacles, seemed positively to flash forth sparkling beams of good cheer.

'Good evening, good evening,' said this parson blandly. 'I looked in to see whether I could borrow a little oil.'

'I am complee—' Mrs Spoker began from force of habit; but she broke off, amazed at the procedure of the reverend gentleman.

'Good gracious!' exclaimed the latter, bounding forward with both hands outstretched to Margaret. 'Mrs – Mrs – er – Hackett, yes, Hackett, as I live. I almost forgot your married name for a moment. First time we have met since before the happy event. Sorry I couldn't be there – sickening! Still so glad to see you now.'

'O – h,' responded Margaret, skilfully disguising vexation as surprise, 'fancy meeting you here, Mr Sloley-Jones.'

'You're staying here?' pursued the other keenly.

'Er – yes. Just for the one night. Are you?'

'No,' said Mrs Spoker.

'No,' agreed Sloley-Jones. 'I just looked in to see whether I could borrow a little oil.'

'No,' said Mrs Spoker.

Sloley-Jones paid no heed to her. He had turned with a

fresh burst of enthusiasm to Peter, radiating flashes of pleasure from his spectacles.

'First time we've met,' he cried, as he seized Peter's hand and commenced to wring it. 'Delighted! How-do-you-do? Splendid. How are you? Well done! I'm first rate, thanks — A1. Hope you're the same? Good!'

# CHAPTER VI

## Tally-ho!

Sophia did not lose her head. True, she glanced at the communication cord above the window of the railway carriage, but only for a moment. There is a wealth of sinister inference about that warning against improper use. It is not so much the five pounds; it is the probability of tedious and perplexing argument with autocratic officials, of police court proceedings, of snapshots in the daily press.

Moreover, to Sophia, who was an eminently reasonable young woman, it appeared extremely improbable that the guard, if summoned, would consent to back the train into Paddington from Ealing in order to regain Peter. Again, it was unlikely that Peter would wait expectantly for this solution; especially now that he had picked up this blonde woman. Ah! That was the thought which rankled in the mind of Sophia, far outweighing the grievance of Peter having missed the train and having kept the tickets in his waistcoat pocket.

Sophia sat watching the uninspiring scenery of the Thames Valley with dull eyes. She gradually mastered her impetuosity with an effort of which only a wholesale iron-monger's daughter was capable. Had she been in the retail trade she would have sounded the alarm signal long ago, or perhaps have thrown herself bodily from the carriage as the train started. As it was, she kept such vulgarly headstrong impulses in check. She sat back in the corner seat of her first class carriage and froze the desire to do anything excitable or undignified with a cold douche of wholesale self-control.

The long suffering nature of the British Public is never more strongly emphasised than when the British Public travels. One has only to undertake a short journey on one of

the underground railways of London to observe a great flock
of human sheep submissively yielding to the insolent tyranny
of one barking whelp at the gate. Great, potent men, on their
way to devastate a whole meeting of querulous shareholders;
fierce, opinionated women, bound for Westminter on acrimonious political deputations, are cowed into obedience by
the lashing tongue of that one, sharp-nosed slave-driver and
meekly pass right down the car.

This affords an amazing commentary on the British public
character; and it is a noteworthy feature that, when protest
is raised, the protestant, for whose sentiments the whole
flock of sheep has a sneaking sympathy, is unquestioningly
regarded as a goat of the worst type. For this reason the
better class sheep prefer to show their utter contempt for the
hound in charge by appearing not to heed him at all, and by
merely obeying his orders as though they happen, by some
coincidence, at that very moment to be desirious of passing
right down the car in their own interests.

Sophia belonged decidedly to the better class of travelling
sheep. She stifled the inclination to make a scene with the
guard, even though she was the sole occupant of her particular compartment. She also determined that when the
official should appear to inspect the tickets, rather than
endure a single sentence of expostulation she would pay her
fare over again.

Meanwhile she stared casually at wet fields and thought of
the blonde woman.

Sophia possessed none of the haphazard bonhomie of the
class into which she had married. There were many girls of
Peter's acquaintance (some of them had learnt the news of
his engagement with unwonted wistfulness) who would, in
Sophia's position, have felt deep vexation at his carelessness,
especially in regard to the tickets, and who might have expressed indignation against his blonde friend for having been
instrumental in making him miss the train. But they, knowing Peter, would not have brooded through the windows all
the way to Swindon with dark suspicions of a prearranged

*coup,* visions of secretive and unlawful pastimes, pre-monitions of every detail of a brief, unhappy marriage being bared to the public eye on flaming posters.

Sophia came of a stock which rejoices in the due adver-tisement of its successes, but counts public investigation of its failures as only less desirable than a Presbyterian conception of the Day of Judgment. While Peter, without courting no-toriety of any description, would have accepted it quite im-passively and would, no doubt, have thrived on it, his wife shrank back into her corner from the thought that her private affairs might be subjected to the investigation of those apparently half-informed but sedulous gentry who fill two pages weekly with a list of the Things which, as they bluntly confess, they Want to Know.

But Sophia was a spirited girl. It was not her intention to see Peter decoyed on the very morrow of his marriage back into the excesses of his unrevealed bachelorhood. She was temporarily in awe of his social standing, but the iron-mongery had not entered into her soul to the extent of com-pelling blind subjection.

At Bristol she would wire to announce that she was returning immediately. This would warn Peter that he must get rid of the blonde without delay and thus avoid the un-pleasantness of an unforeseen passage of arms. Besides, Sophia felt more confident of her ability to deal with Peter in the absence of the blonde. She would take the first train back to London and she would hear, quite calmly, what Peter had to say. Of course she might have to threaten to wire to her mother. Sophia sat more upright in her corner seat as she began to realise the strength of her position.

She would, beyond all question, bring Peter to his knees. He would plead forgiveness, which would be granted in the full love of a woman's nature. Sophia was a connoisseur of matinées.

So Sophia paid her first-class single fare to a rather puz-zled official and withered his attempts at conciliation. At Bristol she imperiously superintended the collection of her luggage and Peter's into a large but neat pile on the London platform, sent her wire and had tea.

The up-train was due to leave at five o'clock, arriving at Paddington at 7.30. Sophia was in some doubt as to whether she ought to send a wire to Lady Bunter, but was stayed from this course by the thought that Peter had possibly done so. The arrival at Rushcombe Fitz-Chartres of two conflicting telegrams was not calculated to improve the outlook for the Wykehams' domestic resettlement.

Eventually Sophia regained Paddington. After a wait of several minutes she secured a taxi. On reaching home she found the flat forsaken, the door locked, the maid absent, Peter—

Sophia had to assist the driver of the taxi to remove the luggage. The driver then cursed her roundly and drove away. Sophia sat on the stairs till eleven o'clock. She did not go to her mother; her sense of justice was very keen; she would hear Peter before taking any step which she knew to be irredeemable. She was very hungry. She was very tired. She was unloved, deserted three months after her marriage. And, as the hunger and the weariness increased, there came to her, together with a lump in the throat, the knowledge that this was all a foolish gloomy surmise; that Peter loved no woman but her, that he was as honourable as she herself, that she was impetuous and unjust and that what she wanted more than all the world was to hear Peter's step on the stairs and to throw her arms round his neck.

But no Peter came up the stairs. The lump in her throat hardened, and her heart slowly hardened too, as though determined to assert its mastery over the remorseless husband. And the shadows of the coming darkness preyed upon that dreary staircase and closed down on her in her self-inflicted misery; while, through the narrow landing window above her, peered the last streaks of mocking daylight, like the suggestive glances of that dreaded Society Peeping Tom, intent on the examination of one of those many, curious Things he Wanted to Know.

At eleven the maid returned and found her mistress crouched on the stairs in a dire stage of fatigue and distress. Through Sophia's poor aching brain the fragments of the conversation which followed echoed like the foolish inconsequences of a French Primer.

'Has the master gone? – Yes, he left at 2.30. – Was he alone? – No, he was not alone. – Was the lady blonde? – Yes, and the small dog should not have been allowed in the drawing-room. – Had the lady luggage? – Yes, and the couple left in a car. – Open the door if you please. – My telegram is in the letter-box. – Give me some meat, some bread, and some wine.'

The wine, which was thin claret, proved to have a woeful influence on Sophia in her exhausted condition. It not merely refreshed her, it fired her to fresh indignation and action. In her regained animosity, headstrong and reckless of the consequences, seeing that the mask was now thrown aside and that her husband had definitely schemed to trick her and to desert her, Sophia took action forthwith. She rang up her mother.

Sophia's mother was one of those ladies who when once roused from sleep go off like a released spring into garrulous conversation. From the moment of awakening she invariably talked at the wholesale ironmonger until he sprang out of bed and ran into his dressing-room in sheer self-defence. Occasionally she awoke in the middle of the night and talked.

On this occasion she had already been in bed for nearly an hour, and her conversation was relapsing into a drowsy monotone. Her husband had given up replying and was hoping sleepily. He had almost lost consciousness when he was prodded in the pit of the stomach by an elbow and told to go and answer the telephone. It is doubtful whether any treatment more trying to the temper than this could possibly be devised. But Sophia's mother was not the woman to brook defiance. After a few moments' vain remonstrance her husband complied. His manner and appearance were suggestive of a satiated sea-lion.

A minute or two later he returned in triumph. It was she who was wanted. Sophia wanted her. Sophia? Sophia had gone to Somerset. Well, perhaps she was speaking from Somerset. Did she say so? No, he hadn't asked her.

'Well, go and ask her while I put something on.'

'Oh, it's you she wants. You go and ask her.'

'I am going as fast as I can. Don't you get back into bed now.'

'Why not?'

'You may be wanted.'

'Wanted?'

'Yes, wanted – required.'

'What for?'

'How can I tell till I've spoken to Sophia? If you haven't got the sense to ask her yourself—'

'I say, for goodness' sake button up that thing in the front. The servants may see you.'

'The servants are in bed.'

'I wish to Heaven I was.'

'Wait now till I return.'

'Yes, I will; but I may as well get into bed.'

'No you may not. You are to wait up. You may be wanted by Sophia.'

'In Somerset?'

'Don't waste time talking. Wait till I return. You may sit *on* your bed if you like.'


'I knew it,' said Sophia's mother, returning after a great while.

'I had to get in. I felt cold.'

'I don't mean that. I knew it all along. Go and put on your clothes this very instant. Don't put on too many, and don't take too long in putting them on. I knew this would come. I sensed it from the first.'

'What would come? Why dress? Sensed what? What is all this – that's what I want to know – what?'

Sophia's mother seized a stocking from the chair where her discarded garments had been placed, and, shooting a slipper the whole length of the room from her foot, balanced herself on one leg and prepared to clothe the other. In this attitude she cried out dramatically:

'Sophia's husband has left her. I knew it. Another woman. Don't waste time dressing. He gave her the slip at Paddington. Go and dress at once. I foresaw this. They left in a car with luggage. Don't waste time. Just put on your shirt and breeches and things. I knew it all along. You will keep me waiting, you know. I shall be so angry if you do. I am not going to put on my corsets or anything. A blonde woman with furs.'

'But when did this happen?'

'Today of course. When do you suppose it happened? Will you go and put on your breeches?'

'But where?'

'Where? I've told you, Paddington. I shan't be two minutes, you know. When you've got something on, go and get a taxi.'

'But is Sophia in Somerset?'

'Are you trying to be funny?' asked Sophia's mother, doing things with shoulder straps.


Towards midnight the parents discovered their daughter in the midst of the formerly consecrated, now desecrated, flat. She had surrounded herself with all the conventional properties of the deserted wife – the *déshabillé*, the tears, the smelling salts. The very break in her voice as she recounted her story was in due keeping with the traditions. Her mother stood with her lips compressed into a hard, narrow line, and listened with a series of quick nods, which seemed to indicate that events had transpired exactly in the manner she had always anticipated. From time to time she inserted a comment to the same effect.

'Tessie says that he seemed in excellent spirits,' said

Sophia, as she reached the conclusion of her narrative. 'The car was hired from Gamble's garage by telephone. The driver, even, seemed suspicious.'

'And well he might be. I knew this,' said Sophia's mother.

'When he told the driver where to go, the driver appeared unwilling. Finally, though, they all got into the car; he, the woman and the little dog—'

'I sensed that.'

'And drove away – away.' Sophia broke down here. Even at this moment she was subconsciously comparing her rendering of the part of the forlorn bride with Miss Marie Lohr's.

'Poor child!' said her mother. Then, turning to her husband, who was standing apart, fingering the sparse hairs of his crown, she continued in a voice subdued into menacing intensity:

'What are you going to do?'

'What?' said her husband.

'Yes, what – what?'

'I – I don't know. What?'

'Oh don't keep repeating. Have you been listening? Have you heard what Sophia has been telling you? Do you understand what is afoot?'

'What is a foot?' repeated her husband with sleepy stupidity.

'Act, act!' hissed Sophia's mother. 'Do something.'

'Yes, but what? That's what I'm trying to get at – what?'

'Your daughter,' said his wife, with a sweeping gesture, 'is being lugged into the divorce court. Lugged! And you stand there and say "what, what?" '

'Well, what suggestions can you make?'

The hard mouth was contracted again during rapid deliberation.

'Get detectives,' said Sophia's mother.

'Oh, detectives – nonsense! Especially at this time of night! You might as well say, "Go and hire a pack of bloodhounds." '

'This man must be found and brought to book.'

'Brought to where?'

'Book, book! Don't yawn. Act!'

The wholesale ironmonger was fingering his hairs again.

'It's all very well,' he remarked very slowly and stupidly, 'but I don't see that we've any definite proof—'

Both women were on to him in a flash.

'No definite proof! Oh, no definite proof!' they cried in varying inflections of irony.

'After all,' he pleaded, 'he saw Sophie go off in the train to Somerset, and he comes home and takes a car. What does that look like? Looks to me like his meaning to go after her.'

Sophia merely tilted her chin in silent and forbearing derision. Sophia's mother leant forward into her husband's face and said 'Poof!'

'The other – the lady – may have been – well, may have been going the same way or something like that.'

'Huh!' exclaimed Sophia bitterly.

'Oh, poof!' cried her mother.

'I bet you' – the nettled husband and father raised his voice – 'I bet you he's down with those people in Somerset by this time, at the baronet's place, and wondering where the dickens she's got to.' He jerked his thumb at Sophia. 'I'll wire there in the morning.'

'That's right,' said his wife. 'Lug it into the public eye.'

'Anyhow it's no good our standing here all night. I've only got my pyjamas on underneath and one thing and another. We can't do anything until the morning, and I'll bet you that everything will be explained perfectly openly.'

'I shall stay with Sophia.'

'Do by all means—'

'No, don't, mother. I'm all right now.'

'I prefer to.'

'I would rather you didn't.'

'Oh, toss up for it and let's get to bed,' said the other parent with growing asperity.

He was a kind man and relented a moment later, bidding Sophia a tender good night and assuring her that his theory was sound. She remained silent.

'After all,' said the good man, 'he can't always be expected to carry on in the same way as us. We must remember that. His ideas are a bit different from ours; he's been brought up in a different – what's that word – environment. He—'

'I thought you said you wanted to go home,' said his wife.

'I'll wire that place in the morning. Sir – what? Sir Stirling Bunter; Rushcombe Fitz-Chartres. I'll wire him first thing, and I'll bet you – yes, all right – coming, coming. Good night Sophie. And don't you worry now.'

Sophia, who awoke languid and irritable, remained in bed; but her mother, who returned to the flat at breakfast time, plunged enthusiastically into investigation. Her first move was to ring up Gamble's garage. No, the car was not returned and they were without news of it. No, they didn't know where it had been bound for; a long journey – that was all they had understood, and, knowing Mr Wykeham so well, they had left it at that. Eh? Oh, the driver was a newish man but quite reliable. Name of Dann. Yes, they'd see he was sent along to see Mrs Wykeham when he returned.

On reaching his office Sophia's father called for telegraph forms and settled himself for composition. He could rattle off a business letter with any man, but delicate social interrogation of this sort was another matter. He rapidly destroyed a preliminary half-dozen forms and then began to ponder the matter really deeply.

In the first place it was necessary to discover whether Peter was at these Bunters; secondly to explain why Sophia was not; and to do so in a style which was at once succinct and apologetic – these Bunters being obviously howling swells – with an underlying suggestion that there was an entire absence of panic but that Sophia was a trifle anxious. The composer scratched his depleted crown with a pencil, and rehearsed hypothetical telegrams aloud to himself with strange facial contortions:

Can you kindly send news wykeham think some mistake wife caught train he missed so returned—

Is wykeham with you wife missed him started to come but missed him so returned home but miss—

Outside the private office a departmental manager, two ledger-keepers, a lady clerk and three travellers awaited decisions on a miscellany of ironmongering matters and chafed audibly like wild animals at feeding-time. Their director tore the batch of half-written messages from his desk and flung them savagely into the waste-paper basket.

'I'll ring up the flat at lunch-time,' he decided, 'and if there's still no news then I'll – I'll send a wire. Come in, Hopkins.'

# CHAPTER VII

## The Roosting

Sloley-Jones?

Peter could not avoid a certain abstraction of manner as he returned the hearty greeting bestowed upon him by the parson in the parlour of the *Stag and Hunt*.

Sloley-Jones? Peter had heard Margaret address the stranger by this name, and to him, too, it seemed faintly familiar. In his mind he connected it vaguely with Sophia. Why he could not tell.

'Yes, it was a blow being prevented from coming to your wedding,' continued Sloley-Jones garrulously. 'You got my wire, I expect.'

Yes, this seemed in keeping with Peter's veiled conception of what the name ought to signify to his mind.

'Thank you, we did, yes,' said Margaret quickly.

'Oh, yes, we did, thank you,' said Peter.

'Of course,' resumed Sloley-Jones to Peter, 'I've heard of you often enough.'

'From my wife?' ventured Peter.

'Well, yes, from your wife of course, and from other sources too,' said Sloley-Jones. 'A man like you can't hope to remain in obscurity, you know. Ha.'

This sounded rather more formidable. Peter shifted uneasily and sought Margaret's eye.

'I met your wife last just before you were married – at a poor children's guild.'

'A poor children's guild?' repeated Peter feebly.

'Why yes, and you were to have been there too. You were detained in the House I expect,' said the reverend gentleman unctuously.

In the nick of time Peter remembered that to this genial

muddler, as to Mrs Spoker, he was Claude Hackett. He was
no longer Sophia's husband; for the time being he was married to Margaret. He felt a return of the subconscious feeling
of pleasurable novelty which the contemplation of the small
deception had given him. All right! He was not over-pleased
to be Claude Hackett, M.P., but the idea of being Margaret's
husband was queer and, alas, enticing. But he must do the
thing thoroughly. Peter shook off his abstraction and
became quite buoyant.

Mr Sloley-Jones's stay in the parlour of the *Stag and Hunt*
lasted barely ten minutes, but during this time he succeeded
in working havoc. The observant Mrs Spoker ascertained
that the name of her guests was Hackett and – unexpected
development – that Mr Hackett was a Member of Parliament. Mr Sloley-Jones appeared to cherish the long ex-
ploded theory that every member of the House of Commons
possesses a secret fund of political intelligence; and despite
the lateness of the hour and his shortage of oil he seemed
disposed to make the most of this opportunity to remain and
pump Margaret's husband upon the secret personality and
policy of every member of the Cabinet in turn. Fortunately
for Peter Mr Sloley-Jones had a habit of framing his questions in such a way as to leave little doubt of the answer he
hoped to obtain. Perhaps a long classical association with
the interrogative particles *num* and *nonne* was responsible
for this helpful characteristic; perhaps, as a parson, he
realised that the best-informed parishioners are invariably the least talkative and therefore require a strong
lead.

At the same time he was little short of astonished to find
this confirmed Radical agreeing with ready complacency to
some of the most advanced principles of the Sloley-Jones
die-hard Imperialism.

'Indeed?' he cried at one point. 'Is that really your true
estimate of the Labour people?'

'Yes,' said Peter. 'Oh, yes, I think – I think what I said just
now.'

'Ah, and that opinion is – beneath a veneer of bigotry – excuse me using such a term—'

'Not at all,' said Peter.

'That is the true conviction of most of the Free Liberals in the House. Is it not?'

'Oh, you bet it is,' said Peter.

'Really? Enlightening! But you wouldn't care to make the admission in the precincts of the House I am sure?'

'Oh, no, rather not.'

'Dear me. This is entertaining – an eye-opener. Humbug it all is though, isn't it?'

'It is, isn't it?' agreed Peter in a cheerful tone.

Mr Sloley-Jones lowered his voice into a rather sinister whisper:

'What is Lloyd-George's real view of the miners' report?'

'I – I don't know.'

'You don't know? Oh, come now. I suppose you won't say. Is that it?'

'Well, yes,' said Peter. 'I – I hardly care to say.'

'Ah. I ought not to ask I suppose?'

'No – er – I think it would really be better if you didn't.'

Sloley-Jones turned again to Margaret, flashing enthusiasm from his spectacles.

'It is splendid to meet your husband, Mrs Hackett – in such candid mood too – glorious! I never expected to find myself in sympathy with a "Wee Free" – encouraging! Hope you don't mind my calling you by that nickname?'

'Not a bit. I like it,' said Peter.

'Ah. Good egg! Well, I must be off – I really simply must. My good woman, are you sure you cannot allow me to borrow a little oil?'

'What sort of oil would that be – lamp oil?' asked Mrs Spoker.

'No no. Loobericating oil.'

'Well, what's the difference, except that I haven't got any of either of 'em?' was Mrs Spoker's reply.

The parson sighed.

'I felt I was in for trouble,' he informed Margaret in a melancholy tone. 'I shall seize up altogether if I don't get some looberication. I walked for about a mile here because I felt myself over-heating – nasty! Besides, my pistons keep making curious noises – tricky business! I don't like it. However—'

'Well, you can't stay here not if you burst a blood-vessel,' said Mrs Spoker discouragingly. 'I am completely occupied. I have just let my last room to Mr and Mrs 'Ackett.' She plumed herself on her mastery of the name.

Peter winced slightly.

'Where are you making for?' asked Margaret encouragingly.

'Ah. Only Downblotton. Downblotton is my headquarters. I am doing a little tour – so awfully nice! I'm looking up some of the architectural remains in this part of the country. Fine local specimens – I daresay you know them, Mr Hackett? You do? Bravo. Well, as I say, I really ought to be going. I simply must. I only wish I could borrow a little oil. I suppose, Mrs Hackett, that you and your husband came along here by road? There's no railway station for miles.'

'Yes, we did. But our car broke down some miles away. That is why we are stopping here for the night.'

'Oh, bad luck!' cried the clergyman. 'I only trust I shan't be compelled to return here under similar circumstances.'

'Indeed I hope not,' agreed Margaret cordially.

'I am completely occupied,' put in Mrs Spoker warningly.

'Yes. By Jove. I should have to sleep in this parlour or somewhere. Ha, ha!'

'Ha ha!' echoed Peter in repudiation of so ridiculous a notion.

Mrs Spoker treated the proposal to a grunt of contempt.

'After all, Downblotton's only five miles from here,' said Margaret.

'Your motor-bike ought to be good for five miles,' added Peter.

'Yes, it's only five miles,' admitted Sloley-Jones. 'Besides I've had a chance to cool down nicely. I think I can safely be going, don't you?'

'Yes, I really think you can,' said Peter.

'Yes. So we will say good night, shall we? Good night, Mrs Hackett – au revoir. Unexpected pleasure! It's made me feel quite cheerful again. I was getting down in the mouth I can tell you – thought I'd broken one of my inlet-valve springs at least. Still I think I only let myself get a little overheated. I'll try and regulate my mixture a bit better. I think I'm a trifle rich. Good night, my dear sir.' He extended a begrimed hand. 'Such a pleasure to meet you. We must have another little confidential chat one of these days – most exhilarating! Good night, my good woman.'

'Don't you come back now,' said Mrs Spoker. 'Because I couldn't allow this parlour to be slept in, not under any circumstances.'

'But if my looberication fails half a mile down the road—'

'Not if you has heart failure in the churchyard,' said Mrs Spoker firmly.

'Well, well, we must hope for the best, mustn't we? I'm a good deal cooler now and I dare say I shan't konk.'

Mr Sloley-Jones faced the door with an effort, then again turned.

'Good night again, Mrs Hackett. Good night, my dear sir. Ah, hallo little dog! Good night, little dog! Is this your little dog, Mrs Hackett?'

Margaret replied with a succession of quick nods.

'Ah!' Sloley-Jones bent and caressed Pansy, who regarded her mistress with questioning eyes and sneezed.

'Good night, little dog! Dear little dog – pretty little dog!' said the parson.

Mrs Spoker held the parlour door widely ajar and cleared her throat.

'Well, well, I ought to be nicely cool by this time,' said Sloley-Jones. 'Good night – er all!'

The landlady accompanied him from the room in a manner which she might well have acquired from dealing with undesirables in the bar. Peter sought Margaret's eyes with a rueful smile. Her expression was that of a hostess at the conclusion of her afternoon-at-home.

The front door was heard to slam loudly and Mrs Spoker was back in the parlour. Two hard lines of inquisitorial interest stood out between her eyes.

'So you are a member of the House of Parliament?' she asked.

Peter blew his nose conveniently, but Margaret came to his rescue with ready confidence.

'Oh, yes, my husband is in the House of Commons,' she said.

'I shouldn't 'a thought it,' commented Mrs Spoker. 'Now which side would you be, Mr 'Ackett?'

'Er – which are you?' asked Peter cautiously.

'Are you for or against the brewers?' pursued Mrs Spoker relentlessly.

'The brewers? Oh, I'm for them,' said Peter without hesitation.

'Oh, are you?' cried the landlady savagely.

Peter's face fell.

'I – I'm – I'm a supp – a strong supporter of – of beers,' he ventured.

'Oh, I don't suppose you're one of these Pussyfoots,' said Mrs Spoker, 'not by a deal. But what I want to know is, why don't you gentlemen up there study the question of the public houses?'

'Oh, but I do,' said Peter. 'It's a subject I – I'm awfully keen on.'

'Then why don't we hear of you doing something more for us?' said Mrs Spoker. 'What was that he called you – a wee flea?'

'Free,' explained Margaret. 'Free.'

'Oh, free? Free with promises I suppose, like the rest of 'em. 'Owever, I shall be obliged, if when you come to the office and sign the visitors' book, you'll please put in the letters and all after the name. It will be a object of interest in these parts.'

Peter glanced at Margaret and bowed. His attitude was intended to appear condescending but failed signally in this respect.

'What time will you be a-going to bed?' continued Mrs Spoker, turning her attention to Margaret. 'We keep early hours here.'

'Any time – now if you like,' said Margaret. She stooped as she spoke and raised Pansy in her arms.

'What are you a-going to do with that dog?' asked the landlady suspiciously.

'Take her to bed.'

'To your bed?'

'Yes, of course.'

'To bed with you?' Mrs Spoker's voice was undergoing rapid inflections of shrill astonishment.

'Yes.'

'You and Mr 'Ackett and that dog in one bed?'

'Certainly. Why? Have you any objection?'

' 'Ave I any objection?' Mrs Spoker turned swiftly on Peter. 'And are you in the habit o' sleeping with a dog?' she cried.

'I – oh yes – rather. This little dog always – always sleeps with – with us.'

Mrs Spoker shook her head decisively. She reproduced her strange doubtful, hissing noise.

'No dog sleeps in my bed,' she stated.

'I dare say not. I admit it's an acquired taste,' said Peter. 'But—'

'Such a thing I never heard of,' said Mrs Spoker. 'Why, it's worse than what goes on down at them cottages. It's unsanitary to my way o' thinking. And you a member o' the House of Parliament!'

'Why shouldn't a Member of Parliament sleep with a dog?' asked Peter rather irritably.

'I allow no beasts in my bedrooms,' declared Mrs Spoker in a tone of finality.

'Then all I can say is, this must be a very remarkable country inn,' said Peter warmly.

Margaret interposed with her customary discretion.

'Very well, Mrs Spoker. Just as you like. But where can the poor little girl sleep?'

'Little girl?'

'Little dog.'

'In the stables,' said Mrs Spoker, regarding the poor little girl with a ferocity which seemed to widen the already considerable extent of apprehensive white eyeball in the latter.

'Oh!' sighed Margaret tenderly.

'There's nothing else worth speaking of in the stables,' went on Mrs Spoker briskly. 'She'll have a deal more room there than what she would have in the bed with you and Mr 'Ackett.'

'She'll be so lonely,' objected Margaret stroking Pansy affectionately. 'She may howl.'

'It don't matter if she do 'owl. No one will hear her from the stables,' said Mrs Spoker triumphantly.

'Can't she sleep on the floor of the room?' asked Margaret persuasively.

'No, madam,' was the firm reply. 'No beasts in my bedrooms.'

Pansy was surrendered and commenced to tune up for the stables with a series of crescendo squeaks. Before leaving to deposit her, Mrs Spoker repeated her request that the visitors' book should receive Mr Hackett's attention. She relit the candle in the office and, inviting her guests to enter, bore away Pansy who was now in full rehearsal.

'Look here, Margaret; this is the very devil,' said Peter. 'I must draw the line at forging your husband's name. There are limits. Besides, I'm not quite certain how to spell it.'

'Well, I'll do the writing,' said Margaret readily. 'After all, my name's Mrs Hackett, isn't it? One can't be convicted for half a forgery, can one?'

'Good idea!' said Peter. 'The only alternative is for me to write it so badly that nobody could read it. Of course I could do that; especially in hotel ink. Still, I think on the whole you had better do the deed.'

'Date – 18th of September,' quoted Margaret as she bent over the massive album and commenced to inscribe. 'Visitors' name – C. Hackett, M.P, and Mrs Hackett. There, Peter. The deed is done. Oh – Room number?'

'Oh, give that a miss and hope for the best,' said Peter.

But it was not to be. Mrs Spoker returned with startling suddenness just as Margaret had restored the pen to its tray. The landlady inspected the inscription keenly.

'Room number two,' she said, presenting Peter with the pen.

'Oh yes,' he murmured in a tone of obligatory surprise, as he proceeded to make the kind of 2 which he attributed to Margaret's style of chirography. Then he turned and met her eye with a rather sheepish smile.

'And so to bed,' he said.

Mrs Spoker had already lighted two candles which she handed to them in candlesticks of discoloured metal.

'What time are you to be called, please?' she asked.

'Oh, I – I'll call myself,' replied Peter.

'H'm. That's as you please of course,' said Mrs Spoker.

'Seems to be about the only thing that is,' muttered Peter to himself as he followed the landlady and Margaret upstairs.

Room number two of the *Stag and Hunt* provided an immediate and striking problem to any mind occupied with the interesting subject of upholstery. The door of the room was so small as to necessitate the parties entering in single file. The carefully closed windows seemed ill-proportionately smaller than the door. Yet by some uncanny means so large a quantity of massive furniture had been conjured into the room that the floor space resolved itself into narrow alley ways between bed and wardrobe, washingstand and chests of drawers. Of the latter there were two, a yellow and a mottled. Nor did it appear possible that these articles had been imported limb by limb and, when once inside, built up into a substantial whole, for every one of them had the solid appearance of having been hewn out of one huge trunk. The double bed in itself monopolised a vast proportion of the available space, a tall, ponderous structure covered with a counterpane of a rather livery yellow shade. In several places this appeared to be vainly endeavouring to conceal forbidding-looking hummocks of mattress which protruded aloft like the humps of camels. The carpet, evidently an afterthought, had been cut round the various appointments and was in consequence sagging sadly at the edges. The usual rush mat, so familiarly distressing to cold bare feet, lay before the washing-stand. The walls of the room were decorated with superannuated Christmas cards of a religious nature affixed with drawing-pins, a large framed picture of a soul with a pitiable squint being conducted by discreetly clad angels through a thunderstorm, and copious texts. Peter was examining one of the latter which hung immediately over the centre of the bed, as Mrs Spoker with a curt 'Good night to you,' retired and closed the door.

Peter and Margaret looked at each other for a moment in silence. Then simultaneously they laughed aloud.

'Under the circumstances, dear Margaret,' said Peter, 'I feel it was hardly tactful of them to put "Suffer little children to come unto me" just over your head tonight.'

'Listen!' said Margaret. 'And when we hear her go to bed you can creep down to the room where we had dinner. I hope you won't be most dreadfully uncomfortable.'

'I hope we neither of us will,' said Peter disconsolately. 'You seem to take all this extraordinarily calmly, Margaret, but I must say it looks to me as if we might be working up for considerable trouble.'

Margaret laughed again.

'Nonsense, Peter,' she said. 'Nobody we know will ever find their way to this place, and if they do they won't be any the wiser. Why shouldn't I have stayed a night here with Claude?'

'And what will Claude say?' argued Peter.

'Claude? Why, he'll be amused.'

'Will he?'

'At any rate he'll understand,' said Margaret, inclining her head to one side thoughtfully. 'So, I suppose will Sophia?'

'Oh, yes – Sophia. Oh, Lord, yes – if – when she hears about it,' said Peter carelessly.

'Well then, there you are. Who's going to cause any trouble?'

Peter hovered restlessly.

'What about that turbulent priest – Something Up-Jenkins, or whatever you say his remarkable name is?'

'Oh, I don't count him,' said Margaret. 'I'll explain to him next time I see him. He'll think it a joke too. I'm sure he's a sportsman.'

'H'm. He strikes me as being the sort of keen idiot who crops up at the very worst moment and drops bricks. Besides, I sort of feel that he knows Sophia and her people. It seemed to come back to me.'

'Oh, Sophia's people?' said Margaret with a slightly mischievous smile. 'Still I don't think you need be worried, Peter. I'll manage Mr Sloley-Jones.'

'It's only you I'm at all worried about,' said Peter.

'Then stop worrying, my dear,' she replied. 'Go and listen quietly at the door and see whether you can obtain any indications of Mrs Spoker, because I rather want to go to bed and sleep.'

Peter and Margaret were not the only persons in the *Stag and Hunt* who were considering the possible activities of the Reverend Mr Sloley-Jones. As Mrs Spoker locked the house door she paused for a moment in thought. Unlocking the door again she opened it and peered out into the night. For a few seconds she listened intently. The only sound that was borne to her ears was a long-drawn, stifled squall, pitched in a high key and succeeded by a rapid peroration of breathless yappings. Mrs Spoker again closed the door, again locked it, and removed the key. Then, as though to make assurance double sure, she turned and locked the door of the parlour, and, gathering up her candlestick from the floor, carried both keys, together with those of the bar and the office, upstairs with her to bed.

# CHAPTER VIII

## Pilgrims of the Night

Creaking movements resounded from staircase and landing. Peter turned from his keyhole reconnaissance at the bedroom doorway.

'All clear, I think,' he announced with a wistful smile.

Margaret had been investigating the contents of the two bags which by the joint agency of Peter and Gladys had been conveyed from the derelict car to the bedroom of the *Stag and Hunt*. She was now awaiting the retirement of Mrs Spoker with an air of apologetic impatience and modified unbuttoning preliminaries of a highly tantalising nature.

Three minutes later these had developed in privacy to an extent which entirely precluded the propriety of Peter's return. Margaret heard the sound of a faint scratching at the bedroom door with a quick turn of the head, and, shrouding herself with instinctive modesty, made her way thither between the projections of furniture.

'Is that you, Peter?'

'Y – es. Can I come in?'

'N – o. Why?'

'I must.'

'You can't yet.'

'May I presently?'

'Why do you want to?'

'Because, Margaret dear, I can't sleep in the what's-its-name-parlour.'

'Nonsense,' said Margaret, raising her voice slightly in protest, 'you can't have tried yet. You've only been there about three minutes.'

'But I can't even try, dash it! The old woman has locked the parlour door and sleeps with the key under her pillow.'

'Oh dear. How very unfortunate,' said Margaret. 'So where are you going to sleep?'

'That's precisely what I'm wondering,' said Peter.

'I'm very sorry for you,' announced Margaret through the keyhole, 'but you can't come and wonder here now, Peter.'

'May I open the door a crack?'

'No.'

'It would be easier to talk.'

'Are we going to talk very much?'

'I'll shut my eyes if you like.'

'Kindly keep the door firmly closed until I tell you you may open it,' said Margaret. 'I am in the middle of un-dressing.'

'Oh, what torture!' came in a muffled groan from the passage.

'Go and sit on the stairs for five minutes and then come back and ask again,' commanded Margaret.

'I think my watch has stopped,' whispered Peter fatu-ously.

'Then count five thousand sitting on the stairs,' said Mar-garet.

'Great heavens, am I Pelman?'

'Now, behave, Peter.'

'Behave! I am capable of behaving myself perfectly decently without having to sit on some infernally draughty stairs counting.'

'Well, as far as I can see, you'll probably have to sit there all night. But you may come in and talk it over with me when I am in bed.'

'And what if Mrs Spoker comes down and finds me crouched on the staircase muttering numerals?'

'Oh, don't meet troubles half-way,' said Margaret.

'That's just what I'm trying to avoid doing,' said Peter, retiring with very ill grace to the staircase.

So on the staircase he sat and heaved a little sigh of discomfiture. And if that sigh had been caught upon the night breeze and borne eastward, it might have encountered another little sigh, emanating from another staircase, the staircase of his flat in London. O melancholy circumstance! Here is a charming young couple, but three months married, sitting dejectedly at ten of a September night and sighing in helpless misunderstanding on two widely separated staircases.

Peter waited until he had cramp in the left leg, when he arose rather testily and returned to the bedroom door. Even a woman, dash it, ought to have had time to get into bed since his last call. He scratched again on the woodwork and opened the door a few inches.

'Wait! Not yet! Go away!'

'I will wait here,' said Peter. 'I will *not* go away. When it's "yet", let me know.'

'What on earth is all that commotion?' he added a moment later. 'Is the room on fire or something?'

'I am just getting into bed,' replied Margaret.

Peter sighed.

'Now I hear a noise like a coon band tuning up. I suppose that is the bed being got into?'

'Yes,' said Margaret. 'You may come in.'

She was sitting up. Her arms were spread over the yellow counterpane. Her bright hair had been brushed back and was held in a plait by a white ribbon. She eyed Peter from beneath her long lashes with a benevolent smile. He returned the smile with critical interest, as he advanced and seated himself uninvited on the foot of the bed.

'So that's what you look like, is it?' he remarked.

'It is,' said Margaret. 'Though you didn't come back here to tell me that.'

'All right, all right,' said Peter. 'I simply remark, in passing, that you look extraordinarily becoming in bed, that's all. Your taste in night-wear is simple, but effective.'

'I didn't invite you in here to exercise your alleged humour on the rather delicate position in which we find ourselves,' said Margaret, firmly.

'No, but it interests me,' rejoined Peter. 'I rather like a

plain sensible nightgown myself. Sophia, now, wears a night-gown that looks like an enlarged spider's web which has caught some blue butterflies. And a boudoir-cap. You simply wouldn't believe the time she took to decide which boudoir-cap I was to see her in at the Bunters'.'

Margaret inclined her head speculatively.

'Doesn't it occur to you,' she said, 'that your wife takes thought on such matters simply with the idea of pleasing *you*? It's precious poor fun for a girl to take all that trouble and be laughed about for her pains.'

Peter stirred restlessly on the bed and his smile vanished.

'Well,' he said. 'I suppose I shall have to go down to the stable and sleep with Pansy.'

'Yes,' agreed Margaret cheerfully. 'Good idea!'

Peter sat pulling the lobe of his ear and watched her for a few moments in thoughtful silence.

'I suppose,' he said at length, 'that having gone so far, you wouldn't allow me to try and get an hour or two's rest on the floor of this room?'

'For once in a way,' replied Margaret, 'what you suppose happens to be absolutely correct.'

Peter sighed again.

'You are lucky,' he murmured. 'I wish I had a bed like that.'

'Then you can't be hard to please,' remarked Margaret testing a hummock. 'You will take to the stables like a duck to water.'

Peter arose from the bed and, thrusting his hands into his trousers pockets, commenced a somewhat restricted pro-menade of the bedroom, swinging his toes in front of him, as though he were kicking odious convention from his narrow path.

'It's all such rot,' he said. 'As far as I can see, Propriety is decided and limited not by the niceness of people's minds but by the nastiness. I may give you a lift in my car and nobody turns a hair. I may dine with you. I may sit on the foot of your bed – that's perfectly permissible. One might as well say a man might not go and see a girl in a nursing home. But if I lie down on the floor with my feet under the bed instead of on it, then immediately all the nasty-minded people in London come swarming and buzzing on to you like bees on a queen or a drone, or whatever it is bees do. One might just as well say, when you come to think of it, that it is immoral for a man to sit next to a woman in a bus. I shan't be anything like as near you as I should be in a bus, and we shall both have just as much on – you probably rather more. If you weren't allowed to travel on a bus with anyone you weren't married to, then there really might begin to be some chance of getting about London on the cheap.'

'On the other hand,' said Margaret gently, 'it would be rather uncomfortable if every man who met you in a bus could claim to sleep in your bedroom. It sounds like a newspaper report of early conditions in Russia under Bolshevism.'

'But with old friends, Margaret – I ask you.'

'Yes, you asked me before,' said Margaret.

Peter halted and stood over her. She looked up at him with a masterful smile of confidence. The plaited tail of golden hair had fallen over her left shoulder. Her strong, beautifully moulded arms, bare to the elbow, were still spread out before her. In the dim light of the candle her face looked pale, but her eyes were bright with what looked like rather heartless amusement. Margaret certainly looked very pretty in bed.

Peter placed his right hand gently upon hers and leant towards her slightly.

'Good night,' he said.

'Poor Peter. I'm really awfully sorry you haven't got a bed.'

'You look it,' said Peter.

'We must be common-sense,' said Margaret.

He leapt at what seemed a possible cue for further argument. Margaret withdrew her arms and placed them between the sheets.

'If we are going to be common-sense,' said Peter, 'I really fail to see why I shouldn't sleep on the floor.'

'No, Peter. I've suffered before now for being indiscreet.'

Peter turned from the bed.

'Of course,' he said. 'I forgot. I understand what you've got in mind now; I dare say you're quite right. Yes. Damn! Good night.'

But he halted near the doorway and examined his thumb-nail critically.

'Though, of course,' he added. 'It's different now. I don't see that it's anybody's business but ours and your husband's.'

'And your wife's.'

'Er – yes. Hers too, I suppose.'

'It doesn't do to be too logical in these affairs,' said Margaret. 'You might as well say that if I elected to walk down Bond Street in my underclothes it wouldn't be anybody else's business but mine. Anybody else would see to that.'

'I don't suppose,' said Peter, 'that anybody else would notice anything unusual.'

'I'm really very, very sorry you haven't a bed, but I don't think the floor would be any more comfortable than the stables.'

'Well,' said Peter, glancing dejectedly round the room, 'I could get to sleep here anyhow. I could borrow a rug or a pillow or something—'

'Oh, I'll give you a pillow to take to the stables.'

'Oh, that's awfully good of you. And what, may I ask, is going to happen when Mrs Spoker hears more noises and comes down to investigate and finds me fooling about in the stables with Pansy and a pillow?'

'All right. I meant it kindly,' said Margaret.

'You mustn't forget this,' said Peter. 'In the eyes of the *Stag and Hunt* we are married. If we go and give Mrs Spoker or Gladys or the old man in the bar a hint that we are not really married, we shall probably be bunged out into the night. Our names are in the visitors' book as man and wife. That blighter – you know – O. Henry—'

'Cathcart Sloley-Jones?'

'Yes – has met us here as man and wife. We shall certainly have to explain to your husband in any case—'

'Well, of course I shall do that,' said Margaret. 'And to your wife too.'

Peter sighed.

'Well, if your husband and my wife, who are the only people that matter, hear about what we have done so far and don't mind, surely in Pity's name, they won't grudge me the small additional licence of lying down in the draught with my head under the dressing-table and my feet sticking so far under the bed that I shall bark my shins if I have a dream.'

Margaret laughed softly.

'Oh, I don't suppose Claude would mind,' she said.

'Well, there you are. My own wife is my own affair.'

'Claude,' continued Margaret, 'is not one of the husbands who say rather silly and unkind things about their wives.'

'Nor am I. Nobody could be fonder of his wife than I am of Sophia. I am passionately devoted to Sophia. Now, do let me have that spare pillow and take a chance for a few hours 'neath the shade of the washing-stand.'


'Peter!'

'Um – h – m.'

'Are you asleep?'

'Why?' asked Peter suspiciously from the darkness of the floor.

'I'm so sorry; I forgot to open the window. That is to say, I tried to, but it stuck. Would you do it?'

'Open the window? Do you want me to die?'

'We must have air,' said Margaret in a tone of sleepy virtue. 'Fresh air is essential or I shall have a headache in the morning.'

'I find I've got quite enough air as it is, without asking for any fresh, and I've got a neck-ache now. All right. I'll do it.

Have patience. I will disentangle my extremities from the towel-horse.'

Two minutes later he resumed his recumbent attitude on the floor, dusting his hands together with faint ejaculations of disgust. From the bed there echoed faint cooing sounds suggestive of gratitude.

With a prolonged effort Peter settled himself and drew his overcoat round such portions of his person as the furniture allowed. Again silence reigned, save for soft, regular sounds of breathing. Suddenly from the night without came the muffled but indomitable voice of Pansy. It was repeated – a long-drawn yell, followed by a series of quick, high-pitched squeaks. With a great whirl of bedclothes Margaret sat upright in bed.

'Peter!'

' 'Ullo.'

'Listen. Can't you hear my darling?'

'Are you addressing me?' said Peter rather grumpily.

'Pansy! Poor little dear. Can you hear her, Peter?'

'No,' said Peter.

'You can't be listening. There she goes again.'

'I think I can hear an owl,' said Peter.

'Nonsense. It's Pansy. Oh, I can't bear to hear her.'

'Oh Lord – all right – I'll shut the window again.'

'No, no. Oh, Peter! We can't let the poor little dear go on doing that all night.'

Peter sat up with a groan.

'Well, how on earth do you suggest stopping the damn little – dear little – poor little brute?' he asked.

'If you were only Claude, you would go and bring her in,' said Margaret.'

'If I were only Claude I shouldn't have cramp in my spine.'

'Peter, can't you?'

'Oh, my dear Margaret,' wailed Peter. 'I – I – I would like a shot if I really thought there was the slightest chance of my being able to get to the stables.'

'Why?' said Margaret. 'Only just now you were thinking of going down to sleep there.'

'I wasn't,' said Peter. 'It may be laid down as about as good a cinch as anything that has never been actually proved that that back door leading to the stables is warranted to baffle Houdini.'

'It's probably only bolted,' argued Margaret with drowsy insistence.

'My dear Margaret,' said Peter with a little groan, 'if a woman takes the trouble to double-lock her parlour and keep the key under her pillow, it stands to reason that the door to the yard is hung all over with burglar alarms. It probably has Yale locks and a portcullis.'

'Listen to that poor broken-hearted little darling,' cried Margaret in tremulous tones. 'Oh, how can you be so stony-hearted, Peter? If you had any love for dumb animals—'

'Dumb! God wot!' remarked Peter.

'You wouldn't lie there talking rubbish. I don't suppose you have any idea what a portcullis is.'

'I haven't,' said Peter. 'But you needn't get so animated about it. I don't think it's anything indecent, and even if it is the fact of sleeping in the same room as a lady would seem to justify a certain amount of licence in one's conversation.'

'You're taking rather a mean advantage of me if you're going to force me to get up and go down myself,' said Margaret.

Peter with a moan stirred himself into activity, lit a candle, and sought his discarded boots and jacket.

'One thing about Sophia,' he said. 'She confines herself to moulting lovebirds.'

# CHAPTER IX

## The Sleep of the Just

Peter halted before the small door at the end of the passage through which Mrs Spoker had borne Pansy to the stables. After examining it by the light of a match until he burnt his fingers, he cautiously tested the bolts which guarded it. Though there was nothing unusual in their appearance, they were curious bolts. The bolt at the foot of the door was loose in its socket and could be withdrawn with one finger. It was, in fact, if anything too loose for Peter's liking; it gave forth loud rattling sounds during the operation, at the conclusion of which the head of the bolt fell with a noisy thud against the woodwork of the door.

The topmost fitting offered a direct contrast. It appeared to have been welded into its socket. Still burning matches in reckless profusion Peter exerted himself upon it in vain. He shifted his position and attempted to work the head of the bolt up and down as a vague but hopeful preliminary to shooting it back. The head of the bolt yielded half an inch with a squeak which seemed to resound through the whole house.

Peter set his teeth and made a further effort. The bolt flew back with a sudden staggering surrender and a loud crash. Peter, partially overbalanced for a moment, recovered himself with a gasp.

The door was still held by a turned key. Why Mrs Spoker, who had so carefully guarded the keys of all the other doors on the ground floor, had allowed this one to remain turned in its lock is one of the mysteries which only arise – but always arise – when a woman gets an idea into her head.

After listening anxiously for any evidences of disturbance on the floor above, Peter turned his attention to this key. It was very stiff. Peter found a very good pencil in his pocket and attempted to employ its aid in the difficulty, inserting it through the eye of the key and thus gaining a purchase. He was handicapped by having to hold lighted matches in his left hand throughout the operation, and when he placed a burning match on the floor and used both hands to the key the match went out and he broke the pencil at almost the identical moment.

'That woman,' he said to himself, 'must have the wrists of Tarzan.'

Perhaps the beastly thing wasn't locked after all. He turned the door handle and pulled. No, it was locked. He fingered the key again deliberately. Yielding to an almost unintentional movement it turned quite easily from left to right, in the direction usually employed for locking a door. Peter sighed, lit one of his few remaining matches and groped on the floor for his two pieces of pencil.

He pulled the door open. Oh, he was not yet in the yard. Here were sculleries or something. He was in a dim atmosphere of tea-leaves, crockery and wet floor-cloths. He struck another match and peered his way down a further narrow passage to the real back door.

Here the bolts were more normal. He opened the back door stealthily. Outside the night was dark, but the way to the stables was not difficult to ascertain. Pansy was still unsettled.

Peter stepped out; then suddenly drew back with a shudder. Rain, fine drizzling rain of the most thoroughly wetting variety, was falling with silent persistence.

He stood for a moment in the doorway and turned up his coat collar. His mind dwelt upon the woman upstairs – in bed. What an extraordinary woman she was. A little earlier that night, as he had sat on the end of her bed watching her, he had been swept by a sudden wave of admiration of the homely, settled, unambitious comfort of her nature. Sophia, the artistic, the emotional, the uncertain, had been mentally subjected to unfavourable comparison with Margaret, lying there so cosy and unartificial in her old-fashioned nighty. But Peter could remember Margaret gay and excitable – too excitable. Since she had retired to do penance she had apparently made the discovery that penance was the best form of existence.

As Peter had seen her tonight, Margaret had suggested a breathing definition of home comfort and of intransitory fondness possessing none of the rather erotic emotions of Sophia's *ménage*. Yes, he must confess, he had looked upon her in her homeliness and for the moment yearned. Now he was gaining early and first-hand experience of the lot which awaited the husband of a Margaret.

He must be willing, nay, was expected cheerfully to volunteer to go forth into the cold, wet night after a little blasted barking dog. What would married life mean to such a man? The episode was suggestive of an ordered routine of kind smiles and dull sweetness. No, the impassioned flexible Sophia was Peter's woman – exacting, querulous, at times bitter; but how much more exciting; and really, when one came to the point, no less reasonable. Sophia would never have demanded this dog-fetching business.

Interesting, though, and instructing to spend a night with old Margaret. Poor old Margaret! She had been awfully badly maligned and had been driven perhaps to overdo the domesticated, strictly ordinary part she had assumed. Peter regarded her still with great affection and a sort of indeterminate sympathy.

And now for her confounded dog!

No wonder they had heard the little wretch. The top half of the stable door had swung open. As Peter looked within there was a desperate scramble in the straw and the sharp yelps of Pansy seemed to change in tone from complaint to welcome.

Peter entered the stable. He struck yet another match and stooping over Pansy caressed her kindly. She licked the proffered hand. From head to foot she was trembling in a manner which resembled one continual shiver. The hairs of her ruff bristled. Her tailless hind-quarters seemed to be subject to a separate and more excessive vibration than that which affected the rest of her small black person. Her pathetic eyes with their usual expression of intense fear glanced shiftily to and fro. She ceased to howl only to give vent to a series of long plaintive whistling sounds through her thin sharp nose.

'Shut up,' said Peter.

Pansy glanced nervously from left to right and whistled again.

'Shut up,' repeated Peter.

He raised his right hand very slowly and softly patted the quivering flank.

Pansy raised a sudden shriek of agony. Peter had no idea how sensitive his little friend was on matters of this sort.

'Look here, stop that, or I really will hit you,' he said.

He slowly raised his hand again. Pansy did not wait. She shrieked and and springing suddenly aside sped out of the stable into the night.

'Damn!' cried Peter following.

He stood for a moment on the threshold of the stable. He looked around him, making little chirruping noises with his lips and clipping noises with his fingers. He failed, however, to catch sight of Pansy. He stepped out from the stable. The rain had increased in volume.

'Come here!' said Peter in a hoarse whisper, groping among what appeared in the darkness to be pig-buckets. 'Look here, do come here. Dear little Pansy, come on. I won't hurt you, you infernal little brute. My God, if I catch you – Pansy! Little Pansy! Here, dearie!'

Far, far away, amid the wet undergrowth of the crab-apple plantation, Pansy fell foul of a tree-trunk and gave tongue.

Peter turned with blasphemous comment in the direction from which the note of fear reached him. He blundered blindly into a hand-pump which stood at an angle of the inn wall. He careered into the largest of the pig-buckets and dislodged a salmon-tin. He found himself lost in a dripping morass of weed and stones, where, at the extreme confines of the *Stag and Hunt*, what had formerly been a portion of the inn yard was now the property of vegetating Nature. He butted against another small out-building, unseen in the darkness, from which issued the throaty anticipations of a doubtful hen. He tripped over a derelict broom. He paused and listened only to receive a large globule of accumulated rain on the bridge of his nose from the branch of a tree.

'Oh, damn this!' said Peter. 'And when I get the little brute I know what it will be. She'll be too wet to get into the bed and I shall have to nurse her on the floor. I'll nurse her, by Gad. Here, little Pansy! Pansy-Pansy! Co-ome along then, dear little dog!'

A wire fence separated the *Stag and Hunt* from the crab-apple plantation. Peter found it somewhat unexpectedly. Having found it he leant against it and again listened intently. All was silent save for the dull hiss of soaking rain.

Lingering in a semi-reclining attitude, Peter suddenly re-alised that he was intensely weary. Almost any situation was preferable to that in which he found himself. Better to return to his hard and draughty bed on the floor – to the stable even. Yet he seemed unable to summon the effort. And as he waited hopelessly, uselessly, leaning against the wire fence he longed for the comfort and cleanliness of the refined spare bedroom at the Bunters' where Sophia lay asleep.

A feeling of blank despair, a sort of shock at the realisation that this was really he and these circumstances were really his, combined with the almost mocking summons of sleep, overcame him. He must make an effort – he couldn't. But what was there to be miserable about? All he had to do was to go back. It didn't matter whether he slept or not. Besides he was so sleepy now that he hardly knew what he was doing.

No, but there was something really the matter at the back of his mind. What was it? He hadn't done anything wrong – nothing that he would be ashamed about to Sophia, or that she wouldn't understand – after a bit. And yet this feeling of intense depression had some connection with Sophia.

'Good heavens!' said Peter to himself aloud. 'I know what's the matter with me. I'm blowed if it isn't that I'm home-sick.'

It was. For the first night since their marriage he found himself parted from his wife – from the wife whom he went about criticising to his female friends. And now when he was really left to his own resources, and his own resources resulted in his getting wet through and extremely exhausted in trying to find another woman's stray dog at the dead of night in a dirty little pub at some Godforsaken village in Somerset, he began to realise what drivel he had talked to Margaret about Sophia.

Sophia was hard sometimes. He had learnt to love her hardness. If she was hard ever it was because she was made like that, and he loved her. Perhaps as she learnt how dearly he really loved and treasured her and how home-sick he was when he spent a night away from her she might grow a little softer.

Margaret now was too soft. Damn her shivering little fool dogs.

Rousing himself with a great effort the happy husband returned to the *Stag and Hunt*.

He manipulated the various bolts and locks with as little noise as possible; to which end he ignored the topmost bolt of the inner door entirely. The stairs creaked ominously as he commenced his wary ascent. He sat down upon the staircase and removed his boots. They were very wet.

As he hovered outside the bedroom door he again seemed to hear sounds of restlessness on the floor above. He turned the door-handle silently and crept into the room.

Margaret ignored his entry. Peter lit a candle and carried it inquisitively to the bed.

Margaret lay back on her pillow with closed eyes and a little smile of blissful contentment playing about her lips. Her head was poised slightly on one side, and her cheek and neck had that soft, pink fullness which is irresistible. Peter shaded the candle with his hand and bent over her, holding his breath.

She stirred slightly and her left hand which lay across her breast moved a few inches. The wedding ring on her finger caught the gleam of the candle light. Peter withdrew his head and straightened himself with thoughtful eyes.

He was thinking of Sophia again. Sophia was lying asleep too in her solitary spare bedroom at the Bunters'. Or perhaps she was lying awake, thinking of him and feeling herself that unsettled sensation of discomfort at being parted from him for the first night since her marriage.

Peter shivered in his wet coat and glanced helplessly around him. He would go. After all, though he and Margaret and Margaret's husband and – after reasonable explanation – no doubt Sophia, too, would fully understand and approve this necessity for his sleeping in Margaret's room, perhaps it would be as well for him to take a chance on the staircase or even to try and snatch a few hours' sleep on the bed vacated by Pansy in the stable. For some reason which his overtired brain refused to analyse he did not want to sleep in Margaret's room now. He somehow felt that it was impossible to sleep in spirit with Sophia with his feet under Margaret's bed.

He looked down again upon Margaret asleep. That soft round of cheek and neck was only comparable to a vision of chocolate *éclairs* to the eyes of a schoolboy. Yet this seemed only an additional reason for departing silently and courting Sophia in spirit and the stable.

Peter sighed deeply.

'This is a fiendish outfit,' he said. 'Wandering about wet through and frantically overtired, with my mind having a sort of irresponsible beano on its own. Oh, what the devil shall I do?'

'What dear?' asked Margaret, opening startled eyes.

'I said "What the devil shall I do." '

'Oh!' Margaret blinked at him several times.

'Where's Pansy?' she said at length.

'Well, Pansy as a matter of fact, is looking out for herself. She didn't want to come in with me, so I let her run off and enjoy herself. She's so happy.'

'Oh, Peter! Wouldn't it be kinder to go and bring her in?'

'No, I don't think so,' said Peter hastily.'And in any case I don't suppose I could find her now if I wanted to.'

'Why not?'

'Because the night outside is about as black as the spot-boy's white gloves on the Saturday evening of a billiard match.'

'Where is she?'

'Last time I heard of her she was enjoying herself awfully among some trees.'

'But, Peter – you're wet!'

Margaret raised herself in bed and stretched out a white hand to the arm of his coat.

'Oh, my dear, you're wet through.'

'That's all right,' said Peter carelessly. 'Not through. Only rather.'

'You're soaking; absolutely soaking. How did you get so wet? Is it raining?'

'Oh no, my dear Mrs Watson; I've been standing under a hosepipe.'

'You must get some of those things off immediately. You'll get pneumonia or something. Now, how are we going to manage about this?'

She was sitting up in bed by this time, sweeping the hair from her forehead with busy fingers. She ceased to do so in order to use the hand for gesticulating at Peter.

'I know,' she said. 'Put out the light and remove your outer garments and hang them over a chair to dry. Then wrap yourself in this blanket and keep warm on the floor. After an hour or two the things ought to be dry enough to put on again.'

'God of battles!' said Peter. 'Are we spending the night, or doing "Saved from the Sea" for the cinematograph?'

'Do what I tell you. Remove your outer garments at once; only kindly blow out the candle first.'

Peter cast one appealing look towards the bed and obeyed. The room was plunged in darkness. He removed his wet coat and boots. As he stumbled to his feet he realised that his socks, too, were damp. He balanced himself on one leg to make closer investigation, tottered, overbalanced, and clutching at the nearest object to hand, sent a china basin from the washing-stand crashing to the floor. Margaret raised her head with a muffled cry of alarm.

'What on earth are you doing, Peter?'

'Nothing, nothing. I knocked over a jug or something. Nothing, nothing.'

'It made an awful row,' said Margaret.

'I think it only *sounded* loud,' murmured Peter.

'Is it broken?'

'I can't see. I shouldn't think so. A bit of it may be.'

'Don't be footling,' said Margaret. 'Hurry up and put your blanket round you. It's hanging over the bed-post. And then go to bed quickly on the floor.'

'Hush!' said Peter quickly in a whisper. 'Listen!'

They listened. Yes. Footsteps were descending the stairs. They drew nearer and halted outside the bedroom door.

Peter paused open-mouthed. The flickering light of a candle shone through the abnormally large crack between the door and the mat. He drew a deep breath. To be subjected to a verbal inquisition from Mrs Spoker at that hour and in those circumstances was more than even he could face. He groped his way stealthily round the bed. Mrs Spoker knocked and he hesitated no longer. He clambered into bed beside Margaret and drew the bedclothes round his neck. Margaret appeared to give her silent consent to such a course. She uttered no remonstrance; nor did she reply to the sound of knocking which was now repeated from the landing.

'Pretend to be asleep,' whispered Peter.

Margaret made no reply. Mrs Spoker pushed the door a

foot open and peered in. The silence was broken only by the sounds of heavy breathing.

Holding her candle aloft, Mrs Spoker advanced a pace into the room and scrutinised the bed and its occupants severely. She could descry the two heads of her visitors lying close together on the pillow. Mrs Hackett's face was slightly raised and wore a smile of seraphic innocence. Mr Hackett's face was downturned, half-buried in the bedclothes.

Behind the landlady, the face of Gladys, wearing an expression of mingled alarm and stupor, appeared, surmounted by curl papers, round the door. She, too, surveyed the sleeping Hacketts. In accordance with her unfortunate habit, she snorted loudly.

'Don't you go making that noise here; you'll wake 'em up,' whispered the landlady, propelling Gladys by pushing movments of her own hind-quarters back on to the landing. 'You get back to bed. It ain't them. If I hear any more of it I'll have Alfred up and make him look downstairs.'

'It's cats,' volunteered Gladys, as Mrs Spoker followed her out and closed the bedroom door silently behind her.

'Cats, rubbish!' said Mrs Spoker. 'You get to bed.'

She stood for a moment with candle raised, frowning down over the banisters, a gaunt figure in her dressing-gown and nightcap. Then, turning with a shrug, she held a brief auditory examination of the state of the bed-ridden old lady above the bar. From this room the sounds of unbroken sleep could be heard even on the landing; and finally Mrs Spoker bore her candle slowly back up the second flight of stairs.

'Peter! Get up and get out at once.'

'Oh, Lord! All right, all right. I was nearly asleep.'

'Come on now. Get up at once. This won't do.'

'All right. Don't prod me, merciful heavens.'

'You may wrap your blanket round you and sleep on the floor.'

'Oh, yes. Thanks very much.'

'Only please do so at once.'

'All right. Don't make a row. You'll have that accursed

old woman down here again. Don't push. I'm trying to find the floor with my foot.'

'If you're sleepy, that's all the better,' said Margaret. 'You'll be able to get off on the floor.'

'What I want to know is – what's going to happen if I'm still asleep when that bleating girl brings in the tea in the morning and finds me on the floor. What am I going to say?'

'Use your sense. Say you are looking for one of your socks.'

'I've got my socks on.'

'Then take one of them off and lose it, and then you can really be looking for it.'

'Oh, confound this, Margaret, really—'

'Hush! Don't make a noise. And mind you get as warm and dry as you can. Good night. Oh – and, Peter—'

'Yes? What? Damn! Half a second. What?'

'Do be careful not to lie down on the broken bit of jug.'

# PART TWO
## 'He Sings all Day'

# CHAPTER X

## The Vicar's Egg

The rain had ceased, but the morning was gloomy and threatening. If Nature forbore, for a while, to weep for the follies and foibles of mankind, she continued to frown heavily upon them. Ponderous clouds hung over the face of the sky. The prospect of one passing smile of sunshine seemed remote.

Yet Nature, even in this embittered mood, found a devotee. He leant through the front parlour window of a small lodging-house in the town of Downblotton and exclaimed,

'By Jove. Rain overnight! Good! The roads wanted it badly. No sun either. Capital conditions for biking. I'm off to Glastonbury for the day, Mrs Wigger. Breakfast ready, you say? Well done. Bacon? Excellent. Thank you, Mrs Wigger. Egg? Bravo. Fried? Good!'

Mrs Wigger, holiday landlady to Sloley-Jones, was a little woman of rosy contentment. Hers was an eminently smoothing nature. Her dimpled hands were generally busy smoothing a table-cloth or a pillow-case; and, failing these objectives, Mrs Wigger would employ them temporarily in making smoothing movements over her own ample bosom. Her manner was invariably sweet and cordial, but studiously noncommittal, as becomes a smoother.

She stood and smoothed herself now, as she watched her boarder stride enthusiastically to the breakfast table and seat himself, bringing the large palms of his hands together with great smacks of delight.

'Would you per'aps care to take your dinner with you – your lunch, that is?' she suggested. 'It will in all probability only make a small parcel and will save you spending whatever it is on whatever it is you get to eat at Glastonbury or wherever it is you get it, that is, if you don't take it as I suggest.'

'Ah – happy thought!' said the reverend gentleman, smiling up at her while yet in eating difficulties with his fried egg. 'Yes. Good idea indeed, Mrs Wigger. What can you give me now?'

'Well, there's always egg,' said Mrs Wigger tentatively.

'Egg! Never too often for me. I love egg. This egg, by the way, is simply tip-top.'

'Very well then, sir. Egg. Hard-boiled, that will be, of course.'

'Hard boiled? No? How too splendid!'

'And what time will you be starting?'

'Let's see now. I'm going to the garage for a bit first. Before I start out today I mean to get thoroughly oiled. I expect they'll want me to clean out my carburettor. I may have to change my plugs. Say shortly after ten, Mrs Wigger.'

'Very well, sir. I'll try and see whether I can't let you have your egg and that ready for you at about shortly after ten or thereabouts. Have you pretty nearly all you require now, sir?'

'Rather,' said Sloley-Jones. 'Rath-err. Except my boots.'

Shortly after ten the parson sallied forth. He wore a pepper and salt Norfolk jacket, which bulged with what Mrs Wigger described reticently as 'the egg and cetera', and which she herself stuffed in a neat parcel into the clergyman's pocket with the air of a benevolent aunt three days before Christmas.

Sloley-Jones had again assumed his marine's leggings against the mud. The sky remained menacing, but he somehow managed to extract a glint of sunshine to catch his spectacles as he waved farewell to his landlady, who stood smoothing herself and watched him out of sight. That the garage had oiled him thoroughly was obvious to more senses than one long after he had turned the bend of the road towards Maiden Blotton.

He slowed down in almost unconscious compliance to his

train of thought as he neared the *Stag and Hunt*. The front
door and nearly all the windows were open to the morning.
Through the window of the bedroom above the parlour Mrs
Spoker shook a duster at him with the facial expression of
one who is cleansing her premises of an evil smell. Sloley-
Jones saw no sign of the Hacketts. They had evidently continued their journey.

His mind was still busy with that charming openhearted
woman and her rather surprisingly nice husband as he
swung round a corner of the road a mile beyond the inn.
Then, quick as thought, came a sudden distraction. Sloley-
Jones gripped his brake, skidded madly, and saved himself
and his bicycle from destruction by plunging an intuitive
leg into the hedge. The small boy remained in the middle of
the road and witnessed the brilliant manoeuvre with a broad
grin.

Sloley-Jones drew his foot from the hedge. He groaned,
wiped his brow and adjusted his spectacles. Then he faced
the small boy and shook his head sadly.

He was a very dirty little boy and his grin was malicious
rather than humorous. His general appearance seemed to
savour of the industrial rather than of the rural. He had the
obdurate demeanour of a Trade Unionist in the bud.

'I say, boy,' began Sloley-Jones, 'you simply mustn't walk
in the middle of the road. It's dangerous – awfully. I was
very nearly into you.'

The boy merely grinned offensively.

'Don't grin now. You must take more care. You – Good
gracious!'

For the boy, unwilling to remain and debate the subject,
was preparing to move on. He twitched a string which he
held in his right hand. The twitch resulted in a sharp yelp
and from behind the legs of the boy was hauled the figure of
a small, expostulating, black dog.

Sloley-Jones opened his mouth wide and, stooping over
his cycle, subjected the dog to a closer examination. At the
same moment the boy moved forward and the dog, stub-

bornly refusing to follow voluntarily, was dragged for several yards on four stiffened legs through the slush of the road.

'Wait a moment,' commanded Sloley-Jones. 'I know this dog. This is not your dog. Where did you get this dog? I know this dog.'

'No, yer don't,' said the boy.

'Yes, I do,' said Sloley-Jones. 'Don't contradict. I know this dog. Did you find this dog?'

The boy hesitated and glanced shiftily from Sloley-Jones to Pansy who avoided his eye with an almost human expression of apprehension.

'I was talking to this dog only last night,' continued Sloley-Jones. 'I was also talking to the lady the dog belongs to. Where did you find this dog?'

'It ain't a dog,' said the boy.

'Oh yes it is,' said Sloley-Jones. 'I suppose you think it isn't a dog because it hasn't got a tail. It is a dog. It is a Dutch dog, known as a Schipperke, from the Dutch word which means a skipper or sea-captain. The dogs are called that because out there in Holland the barges on the canals are all guarded by dogs of this sort. Of course it is a dog – absurd! Did you suppose it was a cat? Now then, where did you find this dog?'

'It ain't a dog,' said the boy.

'You seem to be a very silly boy, besides being very rude and contradictory to those who know better than yourself. I tell you this is a Schipperke dog belonging to a lady I know.'

'If yer think this is a dog,' said the boy, 'yer don't know much.'

'You're the most offensive boy I think I have ever struck,' said Sloley-Jones severely. 'If it isn't a dog, what is it?'

'It's a bitch,' said the boy.

Sloley-Jones turned aside with a sharp, irritated clicking of the tongue. He returned to the charge with a greater assertion of his authority.

'Did you find the d— her?' he asked positively.

'I did that,' said the boy.

'And what do you intend doing with er – her?'

'Train 'er,' replied the boy twitching the string sharply.

'She does not require any training, thank you.'

'Yes, she do,' said the boy. 'She can't even walk proper.'

'Now look here,' said Sloley-Jones severely. 'You must give me that dog at once. I'll see that—'

'It ain't a dog,' cried the boy enthusiastically.

'You must give me that – well, why not? – that beech immediately, and I'll take her to her proper owner,' said the parson.

The boy shook his head slowly.

'Mebbe, there'll be a reward for 'er,' he suggested.

'Nonsense, a reward! Ridiculous! Much more likely you'll get into trouble for stealing her.'

'Any'ow,' said the boy, 'I'll wait a bit and see whether there ain't going to be no reward.'

'But it's ridiculous! I never—'

The parson's hand had strayed to his pocket. An immediate inspiration dawned upon him.

'Now, look here,' he said. 'I do not intend to offer you any money for the do— any money. But if you hand over that do— the little creature without any more fuss I tell you what I'll do, though I don't really consider you deserve it. I'll give you something very nice to eat.'

'What?' asked the boy promptly.

'Well, I'm not quite sure,' proceeded Sloley-Jones, withdrawing the paper parcel with some difficulty from his pocket. 'Egg, for one thing. Are you fond of egg?'

'Let's 'ave a look at it,' said the boy doubtfully.

'There you are,' said Sloley-Jones, opening the parcel. 'Lovely things to eat – scrumptious! More than you deserve.'

Having regained Pansy he administered a severe chiding to a boy who had evidently been brought up to speak in the most rude and argumentative way to his elders and betters, and who showed in addition a strong tendency to interest himself in the study of sex-problems which were almost bound to produce evil influences in one of such tender years. The boy, who had meanwhile withdrawn to the farther side of the road, busied himself in consuming hard-boiled eggs and sandwiches in a manner which only the digestive organs of a boy can permit. Finally Sloley-Jones buttoned Pansy, greatly against the latter's will, into the chest of his Norfolk jacket, and turning his bicycle set off at full speed for the *Stag and Hunt*.

Mrs Spoker had completed her cleansing operations on the first floor and was standing at the entrance of the inn as the parson drew up. She peered at him, as he placed his cycle on its stand, with the expression of a short-sighted pessimist.

'Good morning,' said Sloley-Jones.

'I thought I saw you going the other way,' said Mrs Spoker.

'Yes, you did; but I came back.'

'It's no good your doing that,' said Mrs Spoker. 'I am not yet open to the public.'

'I want to see Mrs Hackett,' said Sloley-Jones, placing a hand inside his Norfolk jacket.

'She's gorn,' was the reply. 'Both she and Mr 'Ackett. And a good job too.'

'Oh, I say. Come! That's not very complimentary. I think they're most awfully nice people myself – topping!'

'That may be,' grumbled Mrs Spoker, 'but the noises there was going on last night in this 'otel was 'ardly creditable.'

'Noises in the night? Why?'

'That's what I wants to know, why. Mr 'Ackett, 'e started of it, goin' out for to let the dog loose. I got that out of 'im this morning when I found one of the bolts o' the door unclosed. But what caused some o' the other noises that took place after, I don't know. It was not them. for I went down to their room to look and there they were in bed and asleep. It wasn't you come back after all, I suppose?'

'I? No fear. No, if I had come back I should have woken you up.'

'Well, whatever it was did wake me up,' cried Mrs Spoker

angrily. 'So much so that I never got a wink o' sleep all night. I made sure at first it must be you outside there with more complaints in your bicycle and wantin' to come in.'

The parson shook his head with a soft smile.

'Sorry to hear you had such an awfully disturbed night,' he said. 'But it was nothing to do with me. I got home all right. Lucky! I was red hot and missing like anything. Why did Mr Hackett let the dog loose? I expect the noise you heard afterwards was caused by the dog.'

He displayed the shivering form of Pansy as he spoke.

'Talking of the dog,' he said, 'here she is. That's why I came back. I suppose Mrs Hackett was rather upset about her?'

Mrs Spoker looked with great severity at Pansy for a few moments before nodding curtly.

'In that case,' continued the parson, 'I wonder that Mr Hackett went and let her out like that.'

'So do I,' said Mrs Spoker bitterly. 'Out in the pourin' rain, gettin' all his clothes wet, which had to be dried this morning before 'e got out of 'is room. And all that disgraceful noise and that at night, and all for a dog.'

Pansy turned a guilty eye from the speaker.

'Well, I suppose Mr Hackett knew what he was doing.'

'I doubt it,' said Mrs Spoker. 'And the noises I 'eard after couldn't a' been made by the dog, for the noise was inside the 'ouse and the dog was somewhere outside, 'aving run away.'

'What kind of a noise was it?'

'Crashing,' said Mrs Spoker. 'And there was a basin broke in the room Mr and Mrs 'Ackett had this morning. But it couldn't 'ave bin that either, because I was in their room 'ardly a minute after the crashing noise come, and there they were, as I tell you, in bed and asleep together.'

'H'm, mysterious – very! Quite queer!'

'So I made sure,' continued Mrs Spoker, with renewed suspicion, 'that you and that bicycle o' yours was at the bottom of it.'

'No indeed,' said Sloley-Jones. 'Anyhow the point is, what are we to do with the dog?'

'Mrs 'Ackett, she spent 'alf a 'our lookin' fer that thing this morning,' said Mrs Spoker contemptuously. 'After their motor-car 'ad come and all, when they was all ready to start; and when she gave it up she left me the address she was goin' to for me to send the dog, if found.'

'Oh, well done – that's prime,' cried Sloley-Jones. 'I'll go after them with the dog – that is if they haven't gone a tremendous distance. How delighted Mrs Hackett will be. What's the address?'

Mrs Spoker retired to the office, whence after a few moments she returned bearing a half-sheet of note-paper.

'Care of Sir Stirling Bunter, Baronet', murmured Sloley-Jones aloud as he read the inscription. 'Oh, Rushcombe Fitz-Chartres. That's only about fifteen miles from here, isn't it? Yes, rather, I know. You can get there across the common – Baynton, or whatever the place is called. Or of course you could go straight on through Downblotton and Turnholme, but that's a long way round.'

'It doesn't concern me,' said Mrs Spoker with a shrug. 'I'm not goin' either way.'

'Which way did the Hacketts take, do you know?'

'No, I do not.'

'Oh, Baynton I expect, though I dare say the road's pretty dud. Anyhow I'll chance it, shall I?'

'Yes, do,' said Mrs Spoker quite encouragingly.

'Right. The only thing is, have you got a basket or anything I can put the poor little thing in? I've been carrying her inside me, here, and I don't think either of us find it very comfortable.'

'That dog's bin more trouble to me than I 'ardly dare trust myself to say,' said Mrs Spoker. 'I 'ave no basket. You must take her inside your clothes as heretofore.'

Ten minutes later the Reverend Cathcart Sloley-Jones sailed through the town of Downblotton at a speed which made the country policeman on duty heave up a nodding head and survey the scene around him with a slow gaze of stupefied horror.

And outside the post office of Downblotton stood, unoccupied, a large and well-appointed limousine. And inside the post office stood Margaret, wrestling with a local telephone directory.

And still more deeply submerged in the post office, in the small telephone box itself, stood Mr Dann, crushing his red moustache against the mouthpiece in an uproarious recital of his movements for the benefit of Gamble's garage, London.

And three doors off Peter reclined, sleepy yet, in the chair of the Downblotton barber.

And at this very moment Sophia's father, in his office at Holborn Viaduct, was flinging his discarded attempts at social telegraphy into his waste-paper basket.

And Claude Hackett, M.P., was asking the hall porter of the Reform Club for details of the trains to Bristol.

And Sloley-Jones, knowing none of these things, but glistening with heat and zeal, joyous in well-doing, was speeding onwards to the Bunters', rehearsing in his mind the full details of the account he should render; with Pansy, reduced to a mere cowering embodiment of dumb panic, in his bosom.

# CHAPTER XI

## Going and Coming

Running an unkempt forefinger over the western portion of a large automobile map, while he held the telephone receiver in the other hand the manager of Gamble's garage gradually succeeded in piecing together the fragmentary remarks of Dann into the semblance of a definite report. He gathered that Dann was conversing with him from a place called Hold On, which, after an interval for consultation with the postmaster, developed into Downblotton. The leak in the radiator had first occurred on the road, miles from anywhere. Mr Wykeham and the lady had stopped in a pub at a place called Half a Tick.

'You don't seem to get the hang of the neighbourhood very satisfactory,' commented the manager.

'No more wouldn't you down in these parts,' replied Dann. 'They still calls their places by the names they was given by Julius Caesar when 'e first came along.'

A further brief interval followed while Dann inquired of the postmaster the name of the little place down the road.

The Downblotton postmaster, who had grown old and grey at his post of duty, considered that efficiency was only to be defined in terms of deliberate and punctilious caution. These quick people with motor-cars who rushed his post office and subjected him to questions in rapid fire he regarded as a serious menace to the peace and rectitude of his native town. He had already experienced quite enough trouble for one morning from the lady of the party, who, having at length arrived at the conclusion that the Bunters were not on the telephone, had left the post office.

The postmaster left his counter and came slowly forward to the door of the telephone box.

'The name o' the place down the road?' he repeated.

'Ah,' said Dann with a sharp nod.

'Down which road?'

'Why, down that road. The place I just come from.'

The postmaster, who by reason of a drooping eyelid could only use one eye for staring, used it at Dann.

'There's a lot o' places down that road,' he said. 'A 'eap of 'em, there is. 'Ow do I know the name o' the place down that road you jest come from? If you don't know the name o' the place you jest come from, 'ow can I tell you the name o' the place you jest come from down that road? There's a 'eap more places than one down that road by a great deal. There's a lot more of 'em than one by a whole 'eap.'

' 'Old 'ard,' said Dann on the telephone. 'I'm just asking Julius Caesar. I find 'e's still 'ere.'

'If folks comes in and says "What's the name o' the place I jest come from?" 'Ow do I know? They ought to know. They come from 'em, not me. What kind of a place was this you jest come from that you wants to know what place it was?'

Eventually the manager of Gamble's elicited the news that the party had stayed overnight at an inn designated the Stunted Hag in a village named Maid's Blotter. No such definite information could be given concerning the destination for which the car was now bound. Rushcombe Fitz-Chartres was beyond Dann's power of memory.

'You'll find it on the map easy enough,' said Dann to his manager. 'O'Brien something it is, I think; or MacPherson – something or other. You'll find it on yer map. It ain't far from 'ere, that's all I know. And if I'd a' known all the rar which would ensue I wouldn't a' rung you up at all, I wouldn't.'

'You needn't 'ave for all the good you've done,' returned the manager.

'No, and I won't do it no more, what's more I won't,' retorted Dann, who between manager and postmaster was becoming somewhat heated.

'That'll do,' said the voice of the manager. 'I don't wish to 'ave no more backchat from you.'

'No more don't I from you ruddy well neither,' said Dann. This concluded the conversation.

In one respect it sufficed. Within five minutes the manager had endowed Sophia's mother with a full share of the information at his disposal.

No sooner therefore had the wholesale ironmonger plunged into the morning flood of his ironmongering matters than a knowledgable lady clerk interrupted him with a confidential whisper. He was wanted on the telephone by Mrs Bone.

'Oh, Lord!' murmured the harassed man. 'All right. Tell her to – that is, ask her to hold the line one moment. Say I'm just in the middle of something important. Hand me those telegraph forms, will you, please?'

He tore now at the sparse hairs of his crown. Seizing a pencil he began feverishly to compose afresh:

Sir Stirling Bunter. Rushcombe Fitz-Chartres. Somerset. Have you any news wykeham he started yesterday for you with wife but got left behind wife started but returned think he started too in car wife has lost track wants to know what to do is he with you—

Wykenam missed wife he—

Is wykeham with you mrs wykeham will come if he is wit—

Wykeham missed train wife caught but—

Yesterday mrs wykeham missed mr wykeham—

'Mrs Bone is through to your private line, sir,' said the lady clerk.

She was. The overwrought husband on lifting the receiver found that his wife was already delivering the peroration of a lengthy harangue.

'Are you listening?' she asked, pausing in the midst of a peculiarly puzzling passage.

'Yes, dear.'

'You are? Then why not say so? Have you telegraphed to the people in Somerset?'

'Yes, indeed I have.'

'Then you have been exceedingly foolish. The last thing I said to you was "don't".'

'Well, I think I still might be able to stop the telegram going.'

'H'm. You can't have sent it off very promptly. Why half-do a thing?'

'Do you want it to go or not?'

'What?'

'Do you not want it to go?'

'What?'

'The telegram, dear.'

'No, of course not. Hasn't it gone?'

'I say – I – I think I can stop it.'

'H'm. When did you send it? How can you stop it?'

'I'll try anyhow. But why do you want it stopped?'

'Why? Because as I tell you I know he is not there. I have found out where he is. Why can't you listen?'

'Where is he?'

'I have told you. He is living with that woman in an inn.'

'Oh, nonsense, my dear. Living! He can't be living like that. He only left home yesterday.'

'He lived with her there last night. I'm not surprised. I knew something of the sort was up.'

'Oh, nonsense, Constance.'

'What?'

'I say nonsense.'

'I can't hear. Do you understand? He went to this inn. They are living—'

'Yes, I say nonsense, Constance.'

'What is monstrous nonsense?'

'All this, about his living at an inn, is nonstrance – nonsous – is non—'

'What? Speak more distinctly. Put your mouth closer to the telephone.'

'What I say, Constance, is that this is nonst – I tell you this is all absolute nonsense.'

'Don't mumble. We must act. Come home here, to the flat.'

'I can't. I don't believe all this non – all this story about the flat – inn.'

'Have you got anything in your mouth?'

'No. Listen—'

'Listen indeed! This line is awful. I think it's mostly your fault. Enunciate.'

'What?'

'Come back here to the flat.'

'I can't. I'm busy. There's nothing really the matter. Where is this inn?'

'Somewhere in Somerset. We must go there at once.'

'Somerset? Well, there you are. What did I say? He went after Sophie.'

'After Sophia? Ridiculous! He went away from Sophia.'

'But not on purpose.'

'Oh, poof! Do you mean to tell me he didn't live with this woman on purpose?'

'He didn't live with her, whoever she was. You can't call it that.'

'I prefer to call it that. It's the most refined way of expressing it.'

'But what evidence have you?'

'Oh, evidence! I have evidence that he and the woman stayed together at the inn last night. That's good enough for me. I know what men are. It's no good your telling me they didn't live.'

'But I tell you this is preposterous, Constance.'

'What? Speak up.'

'He went after Sophie in the car. He must have been going after her. She had all his things.'

'Things?'

'Yes.'

'What things?'

'Clothes and things.'

'What?'

'Things. Clothes and things. His things. Don't you see?'

'What things?'

'Oh, Lord, all his things. He was on his way to the Bunters' no doubt. Is this inn near the Bunters'?'

'I don't understand you. What I am telling you is the clear fact that he lived with this woman—'

'Nonsense, Constance – prepon – you're mistaken. He went after Sophie. He thinks she's at the Bunters' with his things.'

'In that case, pray, why didn't he go to the Bunters' instead of to this inn?'

'Well, perhaps he—'

'With a woman?'

'Well, I—'

'Oh, come home,' said Mrs Bone.


The barber's shop at Downblotton, whither Margaret repaired on leaving the post office, appeared on her entrance to be combining its tonsorial functions with those of the headquarters of the local debating society. Peter had caused the barber to suspend operations and to engage in voluble argument by asking him the best way to Rushcombe Fitz-Chartres. The barber, the barber's apprentice, a completely bald farmer who was having his hair cut by the barber's apprentice, a man with a sheep-dog and the assistant from the bootshop next door were telling him.

Margaret did not wait in the shop. She had made up her mind that there should be no delay in acquainting Sloley-

Jones with the facts concerning the pilgrimage to the *Stag and Hunt*. Here was her chance.

She experienced little difficulty in ascertaining the house where he was staying. Every small boy in Downblotton knew the cycling clergyman.

Margaret went her way down the main street of the little town, a tall, conspicuous figure in her London costume and furs amid the rustic surroundings. There was something in her attitude, a slight unusual stoop, which suggested that she realised this and shrank from it. She, who was the god-mother of a dozen homes for the destitute young, seemed almost to resent, this morning, the attention of small open-mouthed natives. Truth to tell, Margaret's peace of mind was excessively disturbed.

She was afraid of public opinion. She had felt its sting. It was unlikely enough that public opinion would ever glean the interesting details of last night's escapade; but if by any ill chance she found herself confronted with the accusation that she had passed off Peter as her husband and had shared a double room at the *Stag and Hunt* with him, then her own clear conscience in the matter would only serve to accentuate an injustice. At such times conscience must be regarded as an incubus rather than a saving grace.

Fortunately she could count with absolute confidence upon the complacent good sense of her husband, Claude – the dear, charitable, sensible, unemotional man. But there again she must remember that he was a public character. His seat was insecure. An alleged lapse on his wife's part would rob him of the support of every self-respecting Liberal lady in the constituency and would further provide considerable political capital for the threatened female Labour candidate who was the mistress of a Trade Union leader.

With what ecstasy of relief had she first set eyes upon that ill-fated inn. She was beginning now to wish she had never done so. Would that she had spent the night restless and chilly in the foundered car; with Dann, a ponderous chaperon, fumbling at the radiator.

Margaret's spirits rose as she approached Mrs Wigger's. The thought of staying the enthusiastic and communicative parson was in itself a relief. And it was really most unlikely that a committee of Claude's female constituents would find its way to the *Stag and Hunt* or that it would obtain much change from Mrs Spoker if it did.

For that was the chief cause of Margaret's apprehension throughout; love and admiration of that quiet, desperately serious man whom she had married; fear of prejudicing the career which was his pride and ambition.

She knocked at Mrs Wigger's door confidently. She would merely recount their weary discomposure on discovering the scruples of Mrs Spoker and, in merry mood, would thank the parson for having supplied a much-needed touch of reality to their half-formed plot. There would be no necessity to enlarge upon the details of the plot's development.

Mrs Wigger, more than usually non-committal and smoothing herself like an early morning bather, ventured to think that Mr Sloley-Jones was not at home. He had in fact practically left the house well nigh what must be by this time pretty near an hour almost ago.

Margaret's eyes narrowed.

'What time will he be back?' she inquired.

'And that I should really almost hesitate to venture on guessing,' said Mrs Wigger.

Margaret returned slowly to the main street where the car stood. She took her seat in it and waited for Peter. She was thoughtful and strangely depressed. Unpleasant associations crowded to her mind. Last night, before bedtime, she had made light of the friendly parson's blunder. Now it seemed to possess dangerous qualities. She knew what a cheerful gossip that man was.

Other fears possessed her; fears that recalled the misery of being a welcome topic to every cathouse in Kensington.

Margaret was a modest woman. That was, of course, the root of all the trouble. Because she was modest and had pre-ferred philanthropic seclusion to the society of her traducers, the latter had inferred that she had assumed the veil of the guilty penitent. This was an entirely mistaken view. Any one of them would have welcomed her return. Society would as soon think of burning a fortune-teller as of excommunicating a young woman whose romanticism had outstripped her prudence. Margaret knew this, but she refused to go back to the sunshine of some of the gloomiest drawing-rooms in London, if only because it would mean her pleading guilty by inference to a lapse of which she was innocent. She preferred her own quiet backwater in any case. But the injustice scorched her still.

Peter's flippant mood on this horrid morning served only to increase Margaret's distress. This had alienated them ever so slightly. Her insistence on inaugurating a search-party for Pansy before breakfast had widened the breach.

Peter, for his part, as he sat only half listening to the farrago of local geography which was still being poured forth for his benefit in the barber's shop, took mental stock of the complex character of his companion in adventure with a growing frown. Her bright good nature of the previous evening had forsaken her. Surprising woman! How disillusioned might one become on closer acquaintance with the most reliable of the sex. He could rely on Sophia anyhow. He had only to clasp her in his arms and assure her that no unforeseen mishap could ever cause his loyalty and devotion to swerve by a hair's breadth. He felt sure of this — or, at all events hopeful. In an hour's time he would be with her again and could put it to the test. He rehearsed his opening remarks in involved convulsions beneath the barber's towel.

# CHAPTER XII

## As Good as a Mile

At the top of a steep hill, sheltered by deep overhanging trees, Sloley-Jones dismounted and wiped his brow, gazing around him indecisively. He must be nearing the end of his journey. These woods on either side of the road might be part of Sir Stirling Bunter's estate. He would make inquiries. Pansy realising that the moment of her long-delayed but inevitable extermination was now at hand, made one sudden and desperate effort to free herself from the confines of the Norfolk jacket, but without avail.

A few yards further up the road sat a very aged native. Sloley-Jones advanced towards him. The native was one of those old gentlemen who enjoy promiscuous employment connected with hedges and ditches from a somewhat casual Urban District Council and regard themselves with some justification as licensed, if not subsidised, beggars.

The old man failed at first to notice the approach of an almost infallible victim. He was a very old man and his eyesight was growing dim. He sat nodding on the bank, mumbling a quaint West-country jargon to himself and fumbling with a shredded remnant of tobacco in the crown of a hat which must have seen well nigh as many years as its owner.

As the parson halted beside him he glanced upwards, not quickly but stealthily. He scratched with a quivering and horny forefinger at the spot formerly covered by a forelock. His sunken and watery eyes brightened perceptibly.

'Good morning,' said Sloley-Jones. 'I say, could you tell me—'

'Good morn' to you, zur, tho' 'taint a ver' good morn' to be sure.'

'No, not very,' said the parson. Still, it might be worse. I want to find out—'

'It do look to me as though it be blooin' oop – blooin' oop, ye see,' said the old man.

'Yes, it does. Squally! I must hurry. Tell me, where—'

'If 'twarn't so early in the year fer snoo, Aa should a' said it might be it were gooin' ter snoo,' remarked the old man.

'Oh come, it isn't cold. I'm hot personally – perspiring in fact. I wish you would tell me—'

'Mebbe it be a gooin' ter thunder.'

'Maybe. But I think it's more likely to pour with rain. That's why I want to be getting along. Where is Rush—?'

'Aa aint seed no lightenin' in these parts fer many a day,' reflected the old man.

'Where is Rushcombe Fitz-Chartres?' cried the parson.

The old man frowned deeply as though the name was borne to his mind from the dim memories of the past.

'Rooshc'm?' he repeated slowly. 'Ay.'

'Yes?' said Sloley-Jones encouragingly.

'Be you a-goin' ter Rooshc'm then?'

'Well, I hope so. I want to. Must. Why? Is it far?'

'Ay,' said the old man bluntly.

'It is far?'

'Ay. Rooshc'm. Ay, Rooshc'm be a tidy step to be sure.'

'But I'm not stepping. I'm riding.'

The old man admitted this consideration with a nod.

'Ay, it won't be so far then,' he observed.

'Which direction is it?'

'Seein' that you be ridin', mister,' said the old man scratching his head, 'you'd be, you'd be about 'alf-way ther'.'

'Half-way from where?' murmured the parson helplessly.

'  'Alf-way from Rooshc'm,' replied the old man patiently.

'Yes, yes; but half-way from Rushcombe to where?'

This baffled the old man for some moments. He turned his watery eyes up and down the road as though engaged upon a search for a missing landmark.

'Well, wher' else did yer think o' gooin'?' he asked eventually.

Sloley-Jones removed his right hand from the breast of his Norfolk jacket for purposes of gesticulation.

'All I want to know is how do I get from this spot to Rushcombe.'

'What might you have ther'?' asked the old man with sudden interest.

'A dog, but that has nothing to do with it. At least I suppose I ought not strictly to say that because it has, but—'

'A dug? It doan' look like a dug to me.'

'I daresay it doesn't. It's not a very common type of dog. At least it is fairly, but I don't suppose you see a great number of them in these parts. It's a Schipperke.'

'A whatawhat?' cried the old man.

'A Schipperke. But never mind about that. I must get on. Imperative! Where is Rushcombe Fitz-Chartres?'

'Oo, it ain't a dug then?' said the old man, struggling to his feet and examining Pansy with great curiosity.

'Come now, leave her alone, please,' said Sloley-Jones, resisting this attention. The old man's face was now protruding into the hollow of his coat, his head being on a level with the parson's aquiline and somewhat discriminating nose.

The old man poked at Pansy with his bent finger. He was rewarded by the weary groan of one hardened to torture to the point of tedium.

Several of the more irritating of our national proverbs deal with the latent potentialities of the seemingly trivial. If the benevolent Sloley-Jones had only known the immense value of the seven minutes he wasted at the hill-top for the benefit of that aged man, who seemed to find an almost abnormal satisfaction in gouging every available portion of Pansy's anatomy with his horny finger, the parson would have crushed the rural entomologist beneath the wheels of his bicycle rather than yield one precious moment.

As it was, he allowed himself to be led once more into a dissertation upon the nature, habits and nomenclature of the

Schipperke. The old man displayed a keen appetite for information but singularly deficient powers of digestion. Seven minutes passed before Sloley-Jones again buttoned Pansy into his chest with an air of long-suffering finality and said:

'Now I simply really must be getting along. Absolutely. Now do please tell me quite briefly firstly, where is Maiden – dash – Rush – yes – Rushcombe Fitz-Chartres, and—'

'Ay, Rooshc'm—'

'Yes. And secondly—'

' 'Old on, 'old on,' said the old man. 'Aa ain't told ye yer firstly not yet Aa ain't.'

'Which is the way and where is it?' asked the parson firmly, hitting Pansy's head by mistake with a demonstrative forefinger.

'Ay, be all o' that secondly?'

'No, no. Never mind about first and secondly. Simply which is the way and how far is it?'

'Ay, ye said "Where is it" just now.'

'Well, tell me, where is it?'

'Where is it, or how far is it?'

'Oh dear, both.'

'Ay, booth. Ye didn't say that, mister. Ay, booth to be sure. Booth where is it and how far be it.'

'Yes,' said Sloley-Jones.

'Wull,' said the old man. 'Wull now. Rooshc'm. She be over ther'; over ther', ye see.'

'Yes, yes.'

'Ye see. Ye go on, ye see, the way ye do be gooin'.'

'Yes, yes, yes.'

'Ay. Ye go on the way ye be gooin' to be sure. Ye see. And ye go on a matter o' – oo – oo – oo – oo – oo – oo—'

'Yes, yes, yes, yes?'

'A matter o' – oo – oo, mebbe a 'alf-moile, ye see.'

'Yes, yes, yes.'

'An' when ye get on a matter o' a 'alf-moile, why – ye'll be a bit more'n 'alf way ther', ye see.'

'Yes, yes, yes, I see. Yes,' said Sloley-Jones, mounting his cycle quickly. 'Thanks. I quite see. Yes, yes. Thanks. Many thanks.'

'Ay,' cried the old man warningly. 'Ye go on, ye see, the way ye do be gooin'—'

'Yes, yes, yes, yes, yes,' cried Sloley-Jones, working his long legs in great strides on either side of the cycle.

'Ay,' said the old man.

And by the time the latter had moved from in front of the cycle, which was not before the parson had had to pause and dive his hand into his trouser pocket, Lady Bunter had left the Knoll in company with her depleted shooting-party. Seven minutes earlier Sloley-Jones would have stayed her with tidings of one of the two missing couples whose failure to arrive on the day appointed had caused the aristocratic old lady no small measure of bewilderment.

It must of course be her fault. She had muddled. There could be no possible doubt on that score. In the first place they would have wired had it been a question of a missed train. Besides two entirely separate lots of young married people couldn't go astray like that in one day without a word of explanation.

'No, I'm afraid I must have muddled dates,' she said. 'I wrote to both couples at the same time I think, so I probably made the same muddle in each case; repeated my muddle, as it were. They can never have started. But now they may suddenly arrive at almost any moment when we least expect them, not realising, of course, that I muddled and thinking that we shall be expecting them then; so I have made a sort of double muddle.'

Lady Bunter laughed her little cooing laugh at her own expense.

'But haven't you got their letters back, confirming the date?' suggested the old pink man like a design for a Toby-jug, to whom the above confession had been brought on the evening before.

The Bunters were people who had a Napoleonic way with trouble. They never retreated from trouble. They advanced and sought it out. They were generally at grips with trouble of some sort. They challenged other people's troubles besides their own. They always won.

They were both very old-fashioned and pink in the face and countrified. On Sunday they went to a miniature village church and sang hymns about heaven and hell in a manner that suggested that, poor, unscientific, old people, they still believed in these places; which they did. Their lungs were full of clean air and their minds of sweet thoughts and charity. Neither of them had the slightest fear of anything in the whole wide world from Death to earwigs.

'Haven't ye got the letters confirming the date, dearie?' said Sir Stirling.

'No. How careless! I remember I made them into squills.'

'Into what, my love?'

'Into squills. The things you light your pipe with.'

'Spills?'

'Spills if you like. One can say squills, I believe. I always say squills. My mother always used to call them squills.'

'Oh, really?'

'Of course I may be displaying my ignorance. I thought it was squills.'

'Ignorance? Not at all. You're quite right. One can say squills. In fact I believe that squills is really the more correct.'

'Oh no, Sam dear, I'm afraid it isn't. It's my ignorance.'

'Oh, please don't argue, my dearie. It is such waste of time. I happen to know, in this case, that the word is perfectly correct. The point is, what are we going to do about it. Tell ye what. Shall I run down to the study and start unrolling all the spills – squills I mean – the word should be squills, you are quite right, it comes back to me – unrolling all the squills that are there? We might find these people's answers.'

'No, my dear; you mustn't think of taking all that trouble.

It won't bring the people here even if we do find their letters among the spills. All the same I am worried to think in what way I could possibly have muddled. I got the date right in my letters to the others – the people who have turned up; Joe Mock and Mr Goodie.'

'Besides, you don't as a rule make blunders like that. Now if it had been I who had written and asked them—'

'Oh no, Sam, on the contrary, you're very accurate about those sorts of things. I always muddle.'

'Fanny, that's not true and I really won't have you saying such things. You know as well as I do that if anything has got to be done properly and decently in this house you're the only person who can do it. Talk about muddling! I've never known you muddle.'

His manner was quite incensed. A casual observer would have understood muddling to be a domestic virtue of which he sorely felt the lack. After many years the only severe words which ever passed between the Bunters were invariably occasioned in defence of their respective standards of unselfishness.

'Whenever I don't muddle,' said Lady Bunter, 'it's because you see in time what I am doing and stop me.'

'Nonsense. Nothing to do with me at all. This is not very fair of you, Fan. I never interfere. If I did, there would be some muddling if you like.'

'What makes me feel that I really do not think that I made any mistake in my letters to these people was that I believe I showed you what I had written,' said Lady Bunter. 'If I had stuck down something silly, you would have seen it and pointed it out.'

'I should have done nothing of the sort,' replied Sir Stirling sternly. 'Not that there would have been the smallest likelihood of there being anything silly for me to see.'

'Still it must be my fault,' said Lady Bunter shaking her head with a kind and reflective smile. 'Otherwise Margaret would have wired. I don't know about the Wykeham boy, but I should think he would have wired too – Helen Wykeham had very strong views about being careful not to upset people in those ways. But Margaret certainly would have wired.'

# CHAPTER XIII

## 'Sing Cuccu, Sing'

Sir Stirling had white chop-whiskers and a vast red waist-coat, which bulged mountainously like the hindquarters of old ladies of the crinoline period. He lived exclusively in the country, almost entirely within the limits of his own modest estate. Never, since that day when he had experienced the narrow shave with the hansom-cab, had he been to London. For on that occasion he had known a loss which was unique in the whole three and sixty years of his history, a loss which had grieved and sickened him once and for all with the angry tumult of the town. He had lost his temper.

Now and again there would dawn upon Sir Stirling Bunter an awful, haunting suspicion. He suspected his wife. Fanny, too, hated town. At least so she always pretended. But he remembered still the flush of pleasurable excitement which had warmed her still girlish cheek amid all the amusement and gaiety which had preceded that finishing fracas with the traffic. There were times when he still conjectured that her rooted dislike for London life was all a part of her accursed unselfishness.

For in many other matters, great and small, Fanny had proved herself similarly untrustworthy. Butter beans provided a case in point. Sir Stirling loathed butter beans. He had only himself to blame for Fanny getting to know it, but he had let it leak out during the days of their engagement. Fanny had, in consequence, eschewed butter beans and had kept up a rigorous pretence that her soul revolted from them. They had been married ten years before, returning one day unexpectedly to lunch, he had discovered her in the midst of what was nothing short of a secret and gluttonous orgy of butter beans in his absence.

Since that day he had never been able to feel any real confidence in Fanny. If a woman would go to those lengths over a trifle like butter beans, how was he to know her many other impenetrable cravings? What was the honest conviction of her mind in regard to theatres and the gay life? In every one of her dislikes he read a skilfully disguised passion. When she said she would never allow any motor-car to supplant her love of old Dobbie and the rather weather-beaten old waggonette, the distrustful husband's reply had been to allow himself to be welshed into providing her with the noisiest and most unreliable automobile of its year. There had been tears then; tears of love and wistful gratitude mingled with tears of disappointment. How could she explain that this outburst of generosity was the most ungenerous thing he had ever persuaded himself to do? For the only time – the first and the last – their sunshine had known the passing menace of a tiny cloud.

Since then the Bunters had continued to question and combat each other's accursed unselfishness in the abstract.

Never throughout the thirty-eight years of their married life had one unkind word or thought threatened the peaceful harmony of this unyielding war of abnegation. When an agreement on any subject was vital – as, for instance, on the question of procedure in succouring a friend or neighbour in misfortune – it was only to prevent the affair developing into an absolute deadlock that Sam gave way finally to Fanny. This was generally the solution. But the trouble she had to persuade him that he would be doing her a kindness by allowing her to yield to his opinion proved what a stubborn, anti-self-opinionated old husband he was to manage.

They did not entertain frequently. Lady Bunter was fond of welcoming her own intimate friends to the Knoll, but she had a shrewd suspicion that they got on Sam's nerves. Rather than make such a confession, Sam would, she knew, have demolished every nerve in his system. He, for his part, did not encourage shooting parties because he had an idea that, at heart, Fanny possessed conscientious objections to the slaughter of wild game. She had never said so of course. She had never said so because he knew that she had a foolish notion that he enjoyed shooting. He had told her ten million times that he didn't care one rap about shooting. Every time he said it he said it more loudly. It was no good. Fan still refused to believe him. What hell it was for a decent man to be asked to prove worthy of so impossibly sweet-natured and self-sacrificing a woman.

The question whether Sam loved Fanny more than Fanny loved Sam fortunately never arose. It could only have culminated in an explosion.

The shoot which had been arranged for this morning had been deprived of three guns, owing to the absence, unexplained, of Peter Wykeham and Mr Hackett and that, explained, of Mr Mock. Mr Mock had spent many years in the far East and was subject to sudden attacks of gout and liver. This morning he said he had the former, and had the latter.

Undismayed, Sir Stirling roped in two neighbours at the eleventh hour, but set forth rather pessimistically with his remaining guest, Mr Goodie, a Scots gentleman of middle age and rather Winkle-like sporting propensities.

Lady Bunter accompanied them armed with lunch and other mysteries. Her secret intention was to spend most of the period of slaughter in ministering to the confined wife of a gamekeeper.

It did not occur to her to remain at home in the hope of being able to greet any of her four stray guests. She had muddled and, in all probability, had muddled thoroughly. They might arrive in a month. She certainly did not expect to see them for at least a week. Lady Bunter was always getting into trouble with her almanac. She would have kept one of a less complicated sort had she not known that Sam favoured the kind showing saints' days and pictures of the moon. The Knoll was full of articles that neither of the Bunters cared for as much as each thought the other did.

Sir Stirling and Mr Goodie stood by the trap in the front drive, awaiting her ladyship, who was fussing over the final provisions for the comfort of Mr Mock. The latter, a yellow old skeleton with whiskers which sprouted out of his face diagonally like a cat's, accompanied her to the door on a stick. Sir Stirling, who had been attempting to inspirit himself and Mr Goodie with predictions of a glorious day's sport, rather puzzled the Scotsman at this point by telling him loudly how much, on the whole, he hated shooting.

'You will have the place all to yourself,' said Lady Bunter to her afflicted guest. 'Mind you have a good lunch.'

'Tiffin!' cried Mr Mock. 'Good night! I can't eat.'

'Oh, try. I've ordered curry specially for you. I'm sure you'll like it. You'll be hungry by that time. You had no breakfast.'

'I'm hungry now,' said Mr Mock. 'But I can't eat. I simply can't face the thought of *makan* in any shape or form. If I'd realised how sick I was today I wouldn't have had any *chota haziri.*'

'Never mind. You can take it easy here and get well again. You won't be disturbed.'

'Much obliged to you, Fanny. Hope I shan't, I'm sure. But what about that crew who failed to turn up yesterday? They will probably come bursting in and—'

'Oh, no. I don't think there's the least fear of that,' said Lady Bunter. 'I feel confident I muddled by more than one day.'

'Ready, my dearie?' cried Sir Stirling. 'If we're going to start on this dreadful business, we may as well be getting along.'

Lady Bunter, encumbered with baskets, pattered busily down the steps towards the trap.

'Yes, I am quite ready. Joseph is afraid that some of the other people may come, but I'm sure they won't. It's just possible,' she called out, as she took her seat, 'that one of them may send a telegraph. If so, please open it and answer it if necessary, will you, Joseph?'

'I suppose you mean a telegram?' replied Mr Mock with a slightly injured air.

'Yes, if you like,' said Lady Bunter, settling herself with elaborate dispositions of rug. 'One can say telegraph, can't one?'

'Of course you can,' agreed her husband, hiding his impatience to start and directing a sharp glance of reproach at Mr Mock. 'Telegraph is really the correct expression. Telegram is a what's-its-name. Ye don't sign letters with your autogram, do you, Joe?'

'Oh, *mana boli!*' argued Mr Mock. 'Telegraph is an adjective. Of or belonging to a telegram. Telegraph pole. A pole of or belonging to a – a pole for sending a telegram.'

'I don't care. You can send a telegraph. I know you can. Can't you, Goodie?'

'I should say,' replied the judicious Mr Goodie, who was experiencing some difficulty in getting into the trap, 'that the wudd was oreeginally a correption which—'

'Put your other foot up first, Mr Goodie,' said Lady Bunter. 'It's the way this trap is built. I ought to have told you.'

'Anyhow,' shouted Mr Mock, 'anybody with any sense calls it a cable. So if a cable comes I'm to open it, am I? And how the deuce am I to know what to reply?'

'Never mind then,' said Lady Bunter soothingly. 'Are you two all right there? I am so excited and looking forward to your starting to shoot.'

'Hi! *Nanti sikit*! Wait a moment! Here!' cried Mr Mock.

'What?' asked Lady Bunter, checking the somnambulant Dobbie.

'Which of those two men who ought to have come here yesterday and didn't is the one who has been out in the Straits?'

'Oh, Joseph, I've told you. Mr Hackett, the M.P. Don't start talking Malay to the wrong one. Not that it matters because neither of them will be here for some days.'

'Hackett. All right, I only wanted to know just in case. Well, so long, Sam. Hope you have a good day.'

'Oh, I don't much care either way. I'm not really keen on this sort of thing,' murmured the host in reply as the cavalcade departed.

Seven minutes later, when Mr Mock had already conquered his gout and was initiating a campaign against his liver with a strong whisky and soda, he was startled by what seemed to be a machine-gun practice in the front drive.

He arose with an Oriental expletive and sought the library window.

A few minutes later old Francis, the butler, discovered him in an attitude of timorous hostility, like that of a man who anticipates the attentions of the black hand.

'Excuse me troubling you, sir,' said Francis, 'but would you mind having a word with a gentleman who has just called. He come with a dog.'

'Oh, God! Why?' said Mr Mock.

'He happened to find it, sir.'

'Yes, but why do you want me to see him?'

'Seemingly,' said Francis, 'he expected to find Mrs 'Ackett here.'

'Mrs who? Oh, Hackett. Mrs Hackett, yes, I know. Well?'

'He seemed surprised to hear that Mrs 'Ackett was not here, and, when I tells him that her ladyship is also out, he asks whether any of the guests was in the house and I took the liberty to mention you, sir.'

Mr Mock sighed and blew his nose with terrific force.

'Is this the padre with that stinking bicycle?' he asked.

'It is, sir,' said Francis.

'All right. Damn! I'll see him, Francis. Tell him I can spare him a few moments. A dog? What the deuce—?'

Sloley-Jones, who still carried Pansy but who would in any case have been in a soiled condition, was shown, delighted, into the library. He adjusted his spectacles and radiated.

'Mr Muck?' he inquired.

'Mock.'

'Oh, Mock? Sorry. I misunderstood the butler. May I introduce myself? My name is Sloley-Jones.'

'Oh,' said Mr Mock. 'Well, sit down. What have you got there – a Schipperke bitch?'

'By Jove!' cried Sloley-Jones. 'You know the breed?'

'Good Lord, yes. Man I knew in Java had one.'

'Oh, Java? Yes of course that would follow. They're Dutch dogs and Java of course is Dutch.'

'Well, good heavens, d'you think I don't know that?' retorted Mr Mock irritably. 'You'll start telling me William I – 1066 next. Sorry. I've got a liver, or rather gout. Apologise. But don't say things like that. Java Dutch! Have you ever been to Java?'

'N – o, I haven't as a matter of fact,' replied Sloley-Jones cautiously. 'I should love to go. Adore it. It must be a ripping country – priceless! Poor climate though.'

'It's a magnificent climate,' said Mr Mock. 'Finest climate in the world. Call this a climate? What do you know of the *mata hari*?'

'Er – I beg your pardon?'

'I say what do you know of the *mata hari*?'

'You mean the matter of the climate? Sloley-Jones, my name is.'

'*Mata hari*. Means sun. Malay.'

'Oh, I beg – I see.'

'Literally "eye of the day." *Mata* – eye. *Hari* – day. *Mata hari*, eye of the day – sun.'

'Oh, I see. I thought you said, "what do you know of the matter, Harry?" Eye of the day. Yes, awfully picturesque. Poetical quite.'

'So what I say to you is – what do you know of the sun in this beastly country?'

'Ah. Yes, yes. Quite. Ha ha! Still, it's been pretty warm at times lately.'

'Warm! You ought to be in Singapore.'

'Yes, I wish I was,' said Sloley-Jones.

'Well, well. What can I do for you? Have a *stingah?*'

'A – er?'

'A drink. *Stingah* we call 'em. This,' said Mr Mock indicating his mixture, 'is a *stingah.*'

'Yes, it looks it,' said the parson blandly. 'No, thanks.'

'We get the habit out East you know,' proceeded Mr Mock imbibing apologetically. 'Can't get along without it after a bit.'

'Quite so,' said Sloley-Jones. 'Oh, I should love to go there. It must be glorious. However, I brought this dog along here because I chanced to find it in the road.'

'Well, I don't want it,' said Mr Mock.

'No, no. Quite. But as a matter of fact I know this dog. Rather queer. I'll tell you what happened.'

He did so in full detail. Mr Mock failed to display any marked interest in the nocturnal peregrinations of the Hacketts, but grew very apprehensive on being informed of their imminent approach.

'Good Lord!' he exclaimed, as the parson terminated his exhaustive account. 'Then these people may be here at any moment?'

'Oh, rather,' said Sloley-Jones. 'Absolutely. I expected to see them either here or on the road.'

'But I can't deal with them,' cried Mr Mock. 'I don't know what room they go into or anything else. What a bl – blithering nuisance.'

He rose from his chair and executed a series of half-circuits of the hearthrug in a state of indeterminate vexation.

'Oh, I shouldn't worry,' said Sloley-Jones. 'I expect the butler knows. Sure to. Shall I ask him?'

'Yes, yes, do something for Heaven's sake,' said Mr Mock. 'Ring the bell. I suppose you can't jump on your bicycle and go and tell Lady Bunter?'

'I shouldn't worry, you know. From what I know of the Hacketts, they'll make themselves quite at home. Very likely they'll go out and join the shooting party.'

'M'yes. Glad it's the Hacketts anyhow, if it's got to be anyone. I've something in common with Hackett. He's been East.'

'Has he indeed?'

'Course he has. Didn't you know? That's how he made his money so quickly. Rubber. I thought you said you knew him?'

'No, I really only knew Mrs Hackett. I never actually met him till last night, and he didn't say anything then about having been – er – East. Funny!'

'Well, did you ask him?'

'N – o, I didn't really have any occasion to.'

'Well, then, you can't be surprised at his not saying so. A man doesn't as a rule dash up and say "I've been East," unless he's asked, does he?'

'You did,' replied the parson gently.

'Oh, fiddle!' said Mr Mock, breaking off impetuously. 'Do, for goodness' sake, ring that bell.'

'I have,' said Sloley-Jones.

At this point Francis appeared.

'Oh, I say, butler,' said the parson keenly, 'do you know which is Mr and Mrs Hackett's room and all that sort of thing?'

Francis surveyed the dirty clergyman with dignified surprise.

'I do, sir,' he replied.

Francis possessed a fund of restraint which was seldom tested in that house. But his 'I do, sir' was quite patently Franciscan for 'Who the devil are you, coming in to my Knoll and raising domestic queries?'

'Oh, that's all right. Splendid!' said Sloley-Jones shifting rather restively and clearing his throat at Mr Mock. 'So you can fix them up – er – etcetera, can't you?'

'I beg your pardon, sir?' said Francis.

'Not at all. Only, you see – they are on their way here now. I spent last night with them – or part of it at least – so I happen to know – oh yes, I told you of course, didn't I, when

I was explaining to you about the dog? Only Mr M – this gentleman—'

'Oh, do shut up,' said Mr Mock. 'You'll confuse the man. It's all right, Francis. These Hackett people will be here for tiffin, that's all. It's nothing to get excited about,' he added, frowning severely at Sloley-Jones.

'Very good, sir. Everything will be quite prepared for them,' said Francis, unable to resist raising disdainful eyebrows at the object of Mr Mock's scowl.

Sloley-Jones turned from one to the other with a manful effort to screen his discomfiture. He sniggered with palpable exertion. He tested Francis with one heliographic flash from his spectacles but looked in vain for any confirmatory glow.

'Well, well, well, then, that's splendid,' he said. 'I'm so glad. That's simply top-hole. Now I – you know, I really ought to be thinking of – er pushing off. I've got to cycle to Glastonbury. It looks like rain too. Rotten! However. Well, I'm so glad I called and put – er – everything all right. Yes, well – good-bye, Mr – good-bye. Oh, where shall I leave the dog? Good-bye, butler. Will you take the dog? Yes, thanks. Well, good-bye. Good morning.'

He pushed the paroxysmal Pansy into the arms of Francis and fled into the hall. Before the sedate butler had taken two paces in pursuit the machine-gun practice recommenced in the drive.

'Francis,' said Mr Mock. 'I believe that man is *gila*.'

'I shouldn't be surprised, sir,' said Francis.

'Anyhow he's *booso*,' said Mr Mock.

'I'm afraid he is a trifle, sir,' said Francis.

'Quite upset me,' said Mr Mock. 'I think I must have another *stingah*. Do it for me, will you, Francis? Steady with the soda.'

# CHAPTER XIV

## Nemesis en Route

For the second time in two days Sophia found herself westward bound by express train from Paddington. On this occasion she was accompanied by her mother, who sat upright in a corner seat, working her rather pendulous jaw in strange chewing motions of private verbal rehearsal. Sophia's father was there too. At least, he was in the corridor.

Mrs Bone had brought one bag, a loose-leather antique, into which had been flung the nightwear and toilet accessories of all three and two teagowns. It was uncertain where the party was likely to spend the night but in any case they would manage with two teagowns. Mr Bone apparently was expected to manage without a teagown. There had only just been room in the bag for his clean collar and he had to carry one of his hairbrushes in the pocket of his overcoat.

In justice to Mr Bone it must be stated that he had not wished to bring any portion of his property or indeed of himself on this journey. He had not even yet consented to do so. But there he was in the corridor. Seen from the carriage there was a motionless misery about the appearance of his back, like that of an ass standing and doing nothing in a field.

Sophia was pale and very handsome this morning. Her eyes were piercing and defiant. She was in a shocking temper, angry with the whole world. She was angry in chief with herself for having caused all this shameful disturbance, angry with that masterful matron opposite, who seemed to find a certain vindictive satisfaction in her misery.

Yes, Sophia was more angry – more definitely out of temper and methodically cross – to-day than at any period of the evening before. It was a different state of temper and it was directed against a different objective. Peter had ceased to be the leading villain of her inglorious domestic tragedy. Her first outburst of fury against him had slowly died away and another resentment more subtle and even more bitter had gripped her.

Sophia had been herself only subconsciously aware of the change. She had not troubled to analyse the medley of undefined grief and wrath which possessed her heart that morning. The truth was borne in upon her as she sat watching the beady eyes blinking rapidly and unseeing through the window opposite; the heavy lips busy with hypothetical recitation. And, as she watched, Sophia's shoulders shivered suddenly with irresistible aversion.

Peter? Yes, Peter had wrought her a lasting injury no doubt, though Sophia knew that at heart she was still willing, anxious to remain incredulous. But it was the gloating self-satisfaction of her mother, triumphantly assured of his guilt and elaborating its visitation, that had slowly beguiled Sophia's sympathies back to the side of her husband. Why had she been such a fool? Why had she, in the first tempest of remorse, cast all her cards upon the table to be played by that massive, domineering, unsparing hand? There was probably as much jealousy as mercy in poor Sophia's revulsion of feeling.

Why should her mother assume complete command of this wretched punitive expedition? She, Sophia, alone was entitled to dictate terms. Terms? The recreant would get blunt enough terms from his mother-in-law. Then, with a quick yearning, Sophia knew that she wanted to offer generous terms – any terms – any. She wanted Peter back. She loved him.

'Mother!'

Her voice was so sharp that Mrs Bone dislocated a hat feather. Even Mr Bone turned an inquiring head from the corridor. Mr Bone was wearing a grey bowler which became him but poorly.

'What?' said Mrs Bone. 'Don't be so sudden, Sophia. What?'

Sophia leant across the carriage at her mother searchingly. There was an emotion deeper than anger in her dark eyes. She caught her lip between her teeth in a half-hearted attempt at self-control.

'You seem to be glad,' she said.

'I don't know what you mean,' said Mrs Bone. 'You've interrupted my train of thought. What do you mean?'

'You seem to be glad that Peter has done this. You seem to enjoy the idea of this miserable – chase.'

Mrs Bone glanced questioningly through the window and expanded her nostrils.

'I don't think you are in a fit state to talk about it,' she said. 'If you think that I am glad to discover that your husband is a bad hat, then all I can say is that the shock must have been too much for you. I am very excessively distressed to discover it. Not surprised, mind you, in the very least, but genuinely shocked. And the sooner it is thoroughly understood that he shall not and will not be allowed to make your life an absolute hell—'

'What?' asked Mr Bone, peering in with a patient smile from the corridor.

'Go away,' said Sophia's mother. 'I am not talking to you.'

'But, mother, it's no good your pretending you weren't pleased when I got engaged to – to Peter. You were simply delighted about it.'

Mrs Bone shook her head with a wry smile.

'You say you always knew this would happen,' continued Sophia heatedly. 'You were remarkably secretive about it I must say.'

'Well, if you want to know the truth, Sophia, I never from the very outset cared for that man or trusted him the smallest bit.'

'I don't believe you,' cried Sophia, ablaze. 'You turn round on him now and pretend to have been immensely knowing, but when we first got engaged and you found out that he had money and smart connections you were off your chump with pleasure.'

'Control yourself,' said her mother severely. 'Be refined. My chump! Chump!'

'Yes?' said Mr Bone, appearing wearily in the doorway.

He was waved out again with violent fanning movements of a convenient *Daily Telegraph*.

'You never had the slightest inkling that Peter was anything but very kind and very good,' said Sophia, now thoroughly wound up. 'And I still don't believe he is anything else.'

'Then all I can say is, Sophia, that I am horrified to discover that you are the sort of docile, downtrodden wife who encourages a man to be loose.'

'I'm not,' said Sophia. 'And Peter is no more loose than Father is.'

'Nearly every man,' said Mrs Bone, with an introspective blink towards the corridor, 'is loose by nature. Much rests with the wife.'

'Peter may not have meant—'

'Now, don't start that to me,' interrupted her mother. 'You're as bad as your father. I don't want to rub it in about this man, but here he is, living—'

'I don't believe that,' cried Sophia vehemently. 'At least – he may have been led astray.'

'Led astray by appointment at Paddington?' suggested Mrs Bone sweetly.

'There's no reason for you to gloat over it anyhow,' said Sophia with tears of anger.

'Sophia! You don't know what you are saying.'

'Ever since you first heard about it you have been revelling in it. One would think that to discover your daughter was in trouble with her husband was the most glorious thing that could possibly happen.'

'Poof!'

'There's no poof about it,' said Sophia choking back her tears. 'I suppose you think it's smart and fashionable, just because every other couple is being divorced and scandalised about in this filthy world.'

'That is exactly the reason why I—'

'Oh, why must you be so theatrical, mother?'

'Theatrical! If anyone is being theatrical, you are.'

'I was last night,' confessed Sophia boldly. 'Now I'm trying to keep natural. Why do you want to go dashing down to the country with Father and all the rest of this unnecessary rubbish?'

'Do you suggest that I should sit at home and knit?'

'Yes,' said Sophia. 'I wish I'd come alone. I want to see Peter alone.'

'Ah!' cried Mrs Bone, pouncing on this admission. 'Yes, you would like to go and see him alone and would swallow the first fairy-tale he chose to invent. That would be the beginning. You would forfeit your influence over him once and for all. In six months' – Mrs Bone gesticulated dramatically with five suede-gloved fingers and a thumb – 'you would lose him altogether. Then there would be a nice public scandal right enough.'

'Why mayn't I deal with my own husband in my own way?'

'I'm telling you. Because your own way is simply to encourage him to be a loose fish and a fast man and to make a terrific public mess of your marriage.'

'I never asked you or wanted you to do all this. You've taken the whole affair into your own hands, and—'

'My only reason for taking the affair into my own hands' – the express steamed beneath an archway with a sudden roaring rattle. Mrs Bone raised her voice to a shrill scream – 'is to hush it up,' she shouted.

'What's the matter?' said Mr Bone. 'The train was going through that little tunnel so I didn't catch what you said.'

'Will you stay in the passage?' said his wife.

'My dear, I am doing so.'

'Then do it.'

'I am doing it.'

'Then continue to do it.'

Mr Bone turned a sympathetic eye to his daughter. He caught a fleeting glance from her in return. It was the glance of a scolded, impenitent child seeking a friend in need. Mr Bone surveyed his family with bewildered concern.

'What's all this hick-boo?' he ventured to ask.

'Will you go into the corridor and shut the door between it and us?' demanded his wife.

'Aren't I going to be allowed to sit down at all on this blessed journey?'

'You have sat. You did a lot of sitting at the beginning. Why don't you smoke? Go along the corridor to a smoking carriage and sit.'

'Why am I brought?' cried the outcast, apostrophising the whole carriage with outspread hands.

'Why shouldn't Father come and sit down?' asked Sophia bluntly.

'Because I should be very sorry for him to overhear your extraordinary sentiments.'

'You know he'd take my side and back me up,' said Sophia.

'Take your side?' echoed her father. 'Ah, I thought there was a rumpus on. What is all this?'

'At home,' put in Mrs Bone monitively, 'you do nothing but want to smoke like a factory. You have your chance. Smoke.'

'I have been telling Mother that I desire to be allowed to put things right with Peter in my own way,' cried Sophia in clear, challenging tones.

'Well, so I should hope,' muttered her father.

Mrs Bone drew in a long acrimonious breath between her teeth.

'She says,' proceeded Sophia, with a flash of her dark eyes, 'that if it's left to me I shall forgive him. Well, if he's sorry I probably shall. That, surely, is my concern.'

'You've got to find out whether there's anything to forgive him for first,' said Mr Bone.

'Oh!' exclaimed his wife.

She arose with as much dignity as is possible in a train travelling at sixty miles an hour.

'Then, no doubt, you would like me to go and stand in the corridor while you and Sophia plan to lug each other into continual misery and public shame.'

When the party alighted at Bristol Mrs Bone's star was still obviously in the ascendant. She was the first to gain the platform ponderously brisk and alert. She took the platform at a little bound, which set her cheeks and other less evident portions of her anatomy quivering like jelly. She snapped at a solicitous porter as a dog snaps at a fly.

Sophia's fury had given place to the languid dudgeon of fatigue. Mr Bone wore the flushed and constrained air of a defaulter who has just endured an hour's solid cursing from his colonel.

'We will drive from here,' said Mrs Bone. 'Have you got the bag? We cannot rely on being able to hire a motor anywhere else. We will have some lunch in the station buffet. Go and find out where we can hire a motor. Meet us in the buffet. Put your hat on straight.'

'What?' replied Mr Bone, who landed on the platform just as she completed these orders.

She repeated the gist of them.

'I say, don't shout, dear,' said her husband. 'People are looking at us.'

'They are looking at you. Look at your hat. What do you look like?'

'Don't, don't. You confuse me. What a horrible station this is. Which buffy? How can I know where to get a car? We don't even know the name of the place we are supposed to be going to. How can I tell the man?'

'What man?'

'The man. The car man.'

'Get the car. I will tell the man where to go.'

'But, my dear Constance, one cannot go and get men like that. The man will want to know where he is to go.'

'I say, I will tell him.'

'But you will be in the buffy. Am I to bring the man to the buffy? The man will probably refuse to come to the buffy.'

'Of course,' said Mrs Bone loftily, 'if you are afraid of men—'

'I'm not. But what I want to know is – why engage a car till I have had my lunch. I want lunch. It is half-past one. I have an absolute craving for food. Why can't I come to the buffy with you and then go and get the car?'

'Because you will waste half the afternoon getting it.'

'Oh, I see. So I am not going to be allowed to have my lunch until I get the car. A sort of bribe.'

'Ferdinand! Don't make a scene. People are looking. Cannot you understand that if you go and get the car while Sophia and I get some food we shall kill two birds with one stone?'

'Do you want to kill me? Am I to eat?'

'You can take something with you in your hand and eat it while you go and get the car.'

'Oh, God!' said Mr Bone.

'Sophia and I will be in that buffet. You can come and buy whatever you want to take in your hand first.'

'Oh, very well, very well,' said the husband after a moment's reflection.

They proceeded to the buffet. Sophia followed them at a distance, having decided to appear entirely disconnected.

Mr Bone's purchase was remarkably moderate for a hungry man. The garage seemed, on the whole, unlikely to be his first port of call in the streets of Bristol.

'Now,' he said, turning again to his wife. 'What is the name of this place we're going to? The man is sure to want to know.'

'If you are so afraid of the man as all that, you can tell him that it is a village called, I think, Blotto. It is—'

'Oh, ridiculous, Constance! Blotto! It can't be. This isn't Scotland.'

'If it is not Blotto, it is very nearly Blotto. Unless the man is a fool he will know what you mean. Besides, if you will kindly listen to what I have to tell you, you will be able to make it quite clear. It is near a town called something else Blotto.'

'Well then it's probably something Blotto too.'

'Why?'

'What?'

'Why?'

'Oh, Lord, I don't know. Let me go. Here is the bag. How far is this place?'

'I don't know. It cannot be far.'

'Why shouldn't it be? It may be miles and miles.'

'It cannot be far because those two motored from London there in a few hours. Have you no nous?'

'No what?'

'Oh, go; go.'

He went. By the time he returned Mrs Bone and Sophia had grown completely disgusted at the somewhat insipid atmosphere of the buffet; and the former had threatened to report a waitress, who had informed her that it was not a waiting-room, to the general manager of the Great Western Railway Company. Mr Bone, on the other hand, appeared to have been revived and invigorated by his sojourn.

'Come on,' he cried. 'I've got a car.'

'So I should hope,' said his wife. 'By the time you've taken, one would have thought you had got an omnibus.'

'It's the deuce of a way,' continued Mr Bone with malicious relish. 'It will take hours and cost a fortune. Come on.'

'It won't cost so much as divorce lawyers' fees,' said Mrs Bone.

'Mother!' protested Sophia.

'Now don't you start that again,' said Mrs Bone, raising a warning finger. 'Where is the motor, Ferdinand?'

'Outside. Did you expect it to drive into the buffy?'

He marched forth. Mrs Bone overtook him and peered down into his face suspiciously as they walked.

'Ferdinand. I am almost tempted to believe that you have been to a public house.'

'I have,' said Mr Bone. 'I had to. Do you think I am a camel?'

'Why could you not take what you wanted in the buffet instead of keeping us waiting while you went and glutted yourself like a workman? It is most thoughtless and horribly undignified.'

'I can't help that. I wanted it.'

'What have you had to drink?'

'Beer. It's done me a lot of good.'

'You seem to have taken quite enough.'

'I took as much as I could. I had a quart of beer.'

'H'm,' said Mrs Bone. 'So, while we were waiting in that stuffy disgusting buffet of a place, you were standing in a public house saturating yourself with quarts of beer?'

'Yes,' said Mr Bone boldly. 'I'll go home if you like.'

'You can sit on the outside seat of the motor next to the driver,' said his wife. 'You want wafting.'

'I want what?'

'Do what I say. It is nauseating.'

'I'll go home if you like,' said Mr Bone.

# CHAPTER XV

## Coming and Going

Mr Mock paraded the library, his hands at his back, his knees bent and his face contorted by curious twitchings of his feline whiskers. He appeared to be rehearsing; as was, indeed, the case. He was rehearsing the reception of the Hacketts. If, confound it, he was doomed to the task, he would do it with as good grace, as pleasantly and as briefly as lay in his power.

He paused occasionally and directed a sharp glance, from beneath his bushy eyebrows, down the drive. Before very long the unmistakable sound of a car changing gears as it rounded the topmost slope reached his ears. Mr Mock stood at the window, eagerly muttering the opening pleasantries on which he had decided.

Another, less decisive, rehearsal of what should be said and what should be left unsaid in the first few moments of arrival was taking place inside the car. If Margaret had failed to conquer her forebodings she disguised them. She leant forward scanning the house as they approached it with a frank smile of confidence.

Peter did not lean forward. He had lighted a cigarette and was attempting to assume the necessary posture of careless ingenuousness. Both occupants of the car were experiencing the feelings of amateur artistes pluming themselves in the wings for a big scene which might, or might not, be received favourably in the sight of an unreliable audience.

'I shall leave you to get rid of most of the preliminary and explanatory matter, Margaret,' said Peter. 'Get it off your chest in the sort of hearty, "what rotten luck" style. Can you see the front entrance yet?'

'Yes.'

'Is anybody standing there?'

'No. The front door is closed.'

'Good. It would have been just my luck if Sophia had been waiting on the mat. I rather feel that I shall want my second wind for Sophia. I bet you she's the first person we see.'

'That's all right,' said Margaret. 'I'll get out first and ring the bell. You can stay inside the car until we discover exactly who is in the offing.'

'Thanks, yes,' said Peter. 'You might even be able to make your opening speech and then sort of turn and haul me out of the car at the dramatic moment. "And so here is Mr Wyke-ham" style of thing. It all depends on where Sophia is. I bet you she's placed.'

The car drew up. Dann stretched himself and clambered laboriously from his seat.

There was no need to ring the bell. The front door was opened before Margaret had moved from her seat.

Francis stood at the entrance. He turned his head and called to somebody behind him in a voice which could be heard clearly from the car.

'Hann! 'ere, Hann. Mr and Mrs 'Ackett!'

But it was not Francis and his embarrassing warning which struck unpremeditated and paralysing misgiving into the hearts of the car's inmates. No sooner had the front door been opened than a small black object had appeared, quiver-ing with one last forlorn hope, in the portal and, after stand-ing for a moment with ears erect, had darted forward with an outburst of frenzied gratitude and flung itself with exul-tation against the wing of the car.

'Pansy!' cried Margaret.

'How the devil—?' exclaimed Peter craning forward cautiously to gain a view of the hall.

'Some one has managed to get your little dog here, mum,' said Dann informatively.

'Yes, thank you; so I see,' replied Margaret. 'Take all the luggage down and put it into the house, please.'

She turned to Peter with a little gesture of dismay.

'Somebody has been here before us,' she said.

'Yes. With a yarn,' added Peter significantly.

'But who?'

Peter pushed back his hat and stroked his brow. 'Ask the butler,' he suggested.

Margaret nodded.

'Wait here,' she said.

She descended from the car and confronted Francis with a pretty smile. The butler, who was assisting Dann, politely released his end of a trunk on to the driver's foot and bowed his attentions.

'Lady. Bunter and party, 'ardly expecting somehow that you would arrive so soon, though, no doubt, delighted to find themselves incorrect in the matter, madam, 'ave proceeded shooting,' he explained.

'Oh yes,' said Margaret readily. 'I'm so glad they didn't stay in for me – for us.'

'They doubtless would 'ave, 'ad they known, madam,' said Francis, inclining his head deferentially.

'I'm glad they didn't know,' said Margaret. 'I couldn't come yesterday. I missed my train. But, tell me, how did my little dog get here? I lost her last night.'

Francis beamed blandly at the reclaimed Pansy who was worrying her mistress's skirts with every sign of rampant hydrophobia.

'Oh yes, madam; I heard all about the trouble you had experienced with the little – er – the dear – little animal. It was brought here not half a hour ago by a friend of yours. He told us of your movements and that was really what enabled me to expect you and Mr 'Ackett to arrive.'

'Oh. But what friend?'

'A clergyman, madam; a Mr – let me see – Only – no.'

'Sloley-Jones?'

'Ah, yes, madam.'

Margaret nodded thoughtfully.

'I see,' she said. 'Would you like the chauffeur to give you a hand carrying my boxes upstairs?'

'Thank you very much, madam; but we can manage. Will your chauffeur be staying here, madam?'

'No. Oh, no. Thank you. All right. I just want to have a word with Mr – h'm – Hackett. Oh, by the way—'

'Yes, madam?'

'Has Mrs Wykeham gone out with the shooting party?'

'Mrs Wykeham, madam?'

'Yes, Mrs Wykeham. She is staying here, isn't she?'

Francis raised his eyebrows and assumed an air of confidential ambiguity.

'No, madam. We were expecting both Mr and Mrs Wykeham yesterday but – er – they did not arrive, and we are – er – without information regarding their – er – intentions in the matter.'

Margaret turned slowly towards the car. She made a scarcely perceptible movement with the fingers of her left hand, and a round, inquiring face within the car disappeared from view.

'Oh, and one other thing,' she said, again addressing Francis, 'Lady Bunter and the others had left of course before Mr Sloley-Jones called here; so they don't know what happened to – to us?'

'Exactly, madam. Otherwise, I am sure, her ladyship would 'ave remained in. Only me and Mr Mock is aware.'

'Mr Mock?'

'Yes, madam. Another of her ladyship's guests. A gentleman who 'as – er – been East, madam.'

'Oh, indeed? And Mr Mock saw Mr Sloley-Jones.'

'Oh, certainly, madam. For some considerable period.'

'Thank you. I only – I'm so sorry that I – that we should arrive when you don't expect us.'

'Not at all, madam; thank you very much. I quite expected you, having seen Mr – the – the reverend gentleman.'

'Ah,' said Margaret with an effort. 'That's all right then. If you'll kindly see after my luggage—'

Francis bowed and retired into the hall.

Margaret returned to the window of the car. Peter peered expectantly from the back cushions.

'Peter, don't, whatever you do, let the butler see you.'

'What?' cried Peter. 'In Heaven's name what is up now? How can I possibly avoid the butler seeing me? Am I Aladdin or somebody?'

'The butler knows all about the *Stag and Hunt*.'

'All, Margaret?'

'I don't know how much he knows. Sloley-Jones brought Pansy here.'

Peter groaned.

'I thought as much,' he said. 'Confound these priests. And he's about the most dangerous of the whole crowd. Wolsey was a stop-gap curate to that man. May he too be forsaken in his grey hairs and dwindle into a mere advertisement for pants. Where is Sophia?'

'She's not here.'

'Oh, that's better. Come, that's much better. Where is she?'

'She never came here.'

'Never came here?' echoed Peter with amazed distortions of countenance. 'Well, what on earth happened to her?'

'I don't know. The butler says you were both expected but never arrived.'

'Well, I could have told him that I never arrived. But Sophia – Sophia?'

Peter rose to his feet in the car with every sign of extreme perturbation.

'What on earth can have happened to the poor dear girl?'

'Perhaps she put up at an hotel with a young man,' suggested Margaret dryly.

'Oh, shut up, Margaret. This is awful. Do you suppose she went back home? I'd better go back.'

'Well, that was what I was going to suggest,' said Margaret. 'I told you not to let the butler see you for that reason. If they've heard what went on at the *Stag and Hunt* it will

be just as well for you not to disembark here at all. I can say
that my husband had to go back suddenly to town and—'

'And then he'll probably arrive by the next train,' said
Peter wildly.

'I don't think he's likely to come till tomorrow,' said Margaret.

'But we were going to tell these people that we got hung
up and stayed the night at the *Stag and Hunt*. Why all this
evasion? Anybody who thinks that two people can't stay at a
pub without spending the night in the same room must have
a mind like a sink.'

'But don't you see,' explained Margaret gently, 'that, in
order to find out where to bring Pansy, Sloley-Jones must
have gone to the *Stag* and cross-examined Mrs Spoker.
What did Mrs Spoker tell him – that's the point.'

'Did you ask the butler that?'

'Certainly not.'

'Do you think it likely that, even if Mrs Spoker told
Sloley-Jones that Mr and Mrs Hackett performed the extraordinarily usual custom of splitting a bedroom with each
other, the ass would have taken the trouble to repeat it to the
butler?'

'It might have leaked out over the story of Pansy's escape
and that sort of thing. Besides, why should we tell anybody
that it wasn't really Mr and Mrs Hackett who put up there.
If you go back to town now, before anyone sees you, and find
your wife, I will say that I and my husband put up at the
*Stag and Hunt* last night and came on here this morning,
and that he had to go back at once and is expected again
tomorrow. Then, when Claude arrives tomorrow I will tee
him up about it, and you will arrive in a day or two with
your wife and nobody will be a halfpenny the wiser.'

'Of course,' said Peter, 'if you're such an accomplished liar
as all that—'

Margaret smiled dismally.

'I'm only thinking of what will be best and wisest for
everybody,' she said. 'After all, there are lies and lies.'

'Yes,' said Peter. 'And this is one of the lies.'

'You want to go back to town in any case to see your wife; and one thing and another.'

'Yes,' said Peter. 'But one of the other things is that that poop Jones will come crashing down upon us all here one morning and completely upset the entire apple-cart.'

'Well, you can't sit hiding your face in the car all the morning, and the butler is beginning to nose about again,' whispered Margaret briskly. 'We must decide one way or the other. What am I to say?'

'I shall go back now with Dann. I leave you to your own horrible devices. But if and when I return here with Sophia how the dickens am I to know what you've said?'

'It all depends on how much I find the butler and the other man know.'

'What other man? Jones, you mean. These priests are a bane. I forswear religion. Talk about Rasputin the rascal monk. Jones has him beaten to a frazzle.'

'I didn't mean Sloley-Jones. I meant—'

Whom she meant was revealed dramatically enough. Mr Mock, having perfected his plans for a hearty and original welcome, threw open the library window.

'*Mana itu orang, tuan Hackett?*' he shouted in the direction of the car, his yellow face wreathed in a smile of jocular amiability. '*Panggil dia sini. Sia mahow chuckup summa dia. – Tabi la lu. Tabi tuan, tabi s'kali. Tabi, mem.*'

'Gosh!' exclaimed Peter. 'What in the name of all that is zoological is that?'

Margaret had turned with a quick intake of breath. She managed to summon a nervous smile in response to Mr Mock's welcome; then she again sought Peter's agitated countenance.

'I think it's Malay,' she said.

'Your what?'

'Malay. I've heard Claude use language like it. It's a guest here, a Mr Mock. He's been there. He thinks you're Claude, you see.'

'Yes, this settles it,' said Peter. 'I am off, dear Margaret, with all convenient speed. Where's Dann?'

'Here, sir,' said Dann returning at that moment.

'Dann, I'm going back in the car with you to London. Shift.'

'*Mari sini, mari sini,*' bawled Mr Mock.

'Maraschino to you,' murmured Peter. 'Shift, Dann. Tell 'em what you like, Margaret, and put it down to my account.'

'All right. Leave it to me,' said Margaret.

'Shift, Dann,' said Peter.

'*Hi. Nanti sikit. Mana piggi?*' came from the library window.

Dann, the unquestioning, cranked his car, leapt into his seat. With a rasping of studded tyres on the gravel drive the car swung round and straightened into an immediate twenty-five miles an hour down the hill.

Margaret watched it disappear. She mounted the steps into the house and encountered Francis with a ready smile.

'Mr Hackett has gone back again,' she said. 'He heard news from – he heard news which made him think he ought to go back to London at once.'

'Indeed, madam?' said Francis gravely.

'I expect he will be back soon,' said Margaret.

Accents changing from heartiness to bewildered annoyance could still be heard ringing plaintively from the library.

'*Apa matcham? Mana tuan Hackett suda piggi? Apa matcham skarang; mana boli, mana boli?*'

# CHAPTER XVI

## Nests in the Storm

It was not long before the baffled Mr Mock came forth to investigate. Margaret returned his greeting warmly and repeated her fiction of the recalled husband. The Anglo-Oriental displayed considerable disappointment and inquired whether she, too, spoke Malay. He was on the point of returning to the library to reinforce himself against the task of entertaining a lady in nothing but English for the course of an entire tiffin, when Margaret called him back.

'I am so sorry that you were bothered with having to receive my friend Mr Sloley-Jones this morning.'

'Not at all. Glad you got your dog back, my dear lady.'

'Yes,' said Margaret. 'We – I was awfully worried about losing her. I suppose you heard the whole story about how it happened?'

Mr Mock chuckled slyly and rubbed his hands.

'Oh yes. O-o-oh yes, I heard all about it,' he said.

Margaret hesitated and encouraged further comment with an inquiring nod.

'What a night!' added Mr Mock.

'You seem to find it amusing,' said Margaret pleasantly.

'I dare swear I find it more amusing than your husband did,' said Mr Mock.

'Why?'

'Well, my dear lady! Not much catch to be slung out of bed in the middle of the night and sent out in the rain to let the dog loose; eh? Ha ha!'

'Ha ha!' responded Margaret. 'Still, my husband got out – got up of his own accord. We couldn't sleep. The dog was howling.'

'Oh, was that it? No wonder the poor feller got slung out of bed. I've had much the same experience with tigers before now. Only they were even worse.'

'Yes,' said Margaret. 'I think I would rather deal with Pansy than a tiger.'

'Sometimes in the jungle,' Mr Mock went on reminiscently, 'the blighters used to keep me awake all night. All night. Not a wink of sleep. Glad to hear you didn't suffer to that extent.'

'I beg your pardon,' said Margaret curiously.

'Ha ha!' said Mr Mock with a mischievous twinkle in his somewhat rheumy eye. 'You weren't long in getting to sleep after the dog business, believe me. Ha ha ha! I seem to know more about what happened last night than you do yourself; eh?'

'You seem to know quite enough,' said Margaret in a manner of demure reproof.

Mr Mock returned to the library in high spirits. Delightful woman! He was no longer assailed with doubts as to his ability to pilot her felicitously through the *tête-à-tête* tiffin. He was quite stimulated by the prospect of tiffin. He anticipated tiffin. He drank her health.

Presently he saw Margaret leave the house and seek a wicker chair on the terrace overlooking the broad sweep of venerable velvet turf at the front of the house. She had already changed her travelling costume for a coat and skirt of rough tweed. Stockings of a striking plum-colour were displayed. On her feet were brogues of the type which flaunt those rather unnecessary tasselled tongues.

Mr Mock, at the library window, watched her progress, rubbing his nose critically with his forefinger. There was still that little stoop, unnatural and slightly furtive, in Margaret's walk, as though she knew she was being scrutinised but desired to appear unconscious of the fact.

The sky was cheerless and overcast. The wind was stirring the elms to an extent which caused incessant perturbation to a protesting colony of rooks; but Margaret paid small heed to the weather. She took her seat in the wicker chair

and surveyed with troubled eyes the fair prospect of lawn and
shrubbery and the foul prospect of domestic intrigue and
equivocation to which her folly had committed her. She deliberated with a deepening frown. She looked rather like
Violet Hopson at that stage of the film when she realises that
unless she can get the hero to pull the favourite the squire
will prove who her mother was by blackmailing the bishop.

Margaret's thoughts were undoubtedly gloomy, but the
atmosphere of the Knoll awakened a half-forgotten suggestion of peace and rest in the midst of trouble. She had known
the grateful influence of that mellow garden before, its sweet
immutable repose, quelling all the vicious, emotional flag-
rancy of London, as its owners were wont to quell the strife of
neighbours, by sheer impassiveness.

She sat on in silence save for the breeze and the rooks.
Away down in the shrubbery a bent old gardener was performing vague, childish manoeuvres with flower-pots. A
shaggy cocker spaniel appeared from somewhere and,
having investigated Pansy with unemotional civility, rubbed
his back ingratiatingly against Margaret's chair and licked
her hand. In the midst of her dark reflections Margaret
closed her eyes and surrendered herself to the blissful
influence of the old country garden.

Who could willingly engage in deceptions here, however
pressing the need? The fact that a mislaid dog had been
found and restored by a friendly parson was surely not a
circumstance which called for a full investigation of her
movements for the last twenty-four hours. Why worry? She
would not be cross-examined on the subject. She would tell
Lady Bunter, perhaps, in confidence what had occurred.
There would be no necessity to elaborate a fiction for the
benefit of the rest of the party.

Claude she could rely upon. She could picture his thin,
keen face knitted in perplexity and slowly melting into one
of his brief smiles of conciliatory amusement. Mrs Spoker
was unlikely to be heard of again. Sloley-Jones?

Yes, it would be as well to circumvent Sloley-Jones before

he and his overheated bicycle went sailing more dangerously afield. She would take Claude over to Downblotton one morning and they would explain matters.

But stay! Sloley-Jones knew the secret which that disastrous mountainous double bed at the *Stag* had to tell. Caution was required here. Save for the actual witnesses of that fatal simulation of sleep Sloley-Jones was the most formidable figure in the field. The butler and Mr Mock had not set eyes on the alleged husband. Sloley-Jones had held him in exuberant conversation for ten minutes. Mrs Spoker had subsequently told Sloley-Jones about the bed. Perhaps, after the manner of the landlady with a tale to unfold, she had conducted him upstairs and shown him the bed. At all events he knew all there was to know about the bed and possibly surmised supplementary details for himself. Yes, caution was required here.

Peter too. She had allowed the hare-brained, irresponsible creature to dash away without pausing to formulate any definite line of defence, should the unfortunate occasion arise. There was no knowing what incongruities of explanation might not be promulgated at the very outset for the benefit of the inquisitorial Sophia.

An ugly belt of cloud came bowling over the elm trees. The rooks, blacker and more distrait beneath its shadow, increased their hoarse lamentation like the stricken survivors of a devastated village. The old gardener raised his head, dropped a flower-pot, and shuffled away into shelter. The spaniel ambled off with a suggestion of *sauve qui peut* about his apologetic hindquarters. Down came the rain. Once more Nature was weeping for the follies of Humanity.

For the innocent follies in chief, no doubt. It is the innocent folly which causes most of the tears. Margaret went indoors, unsettled still.

Ere long Francis performed a brief selection upon a muffled and deferential gong in the hall, summoning Mrs Hackett to her lunch and Mr Mock to his tiffin.

The progress of the meal proved to be less fluent than the

latter had anticipated. Mrs Hackett responded to his several ventures in conversational urbanity much in the spirit of one ingratiating a talkative child. It seemed as though the curtain of some lurking care was shaking her sensibility from the sunshafts of his gallant humour. Mr Mock languished beneath the strain and after relapsing into a distressing silence sought relief in abusing his food.

'Curry!' he snorted. 'Call this curry? They can't make curry in this benighted country. This is not curry – not even hot. No Bombay Duck! Just as well perhaps. Insult to any decent Bombay Duck to be asked to be eaten with hash. I'd show 'em how to make a curry. I wish I had my boy here. Have you and your husband got a boy, Mrs Hackett?'

'A boy? No,' replied Margaret modestly. 'We've only been married for three months.'

'Oh, good night! I didn't mean – all right – never mind,' said Mr Mock with some confusion. 'Anyhow it's quite evident now that you can't possibly have one.'

Margaret laid her knife and fork (Mr Mock was using a spoon) on her plate in slow astonishment and blushed.

'I'm afraid I don't understand your observation at all,' she said.

'I know,' said Mr Mock readily, waving a conciliatory hand. 'You don't understand. That's the trouble. Never mind. I thought you'd know what I meant. You must get your husband to explain to you. It's a sort of custom. Anybody who has been East will tell you. I thought everybody over here knew all about it.'

Margaret sat back in her chair and looked round anxiously for the absent Francis.

'I see you still don't savvy what I'm driving at,' pursued Mr Mock. 'I'll explain.'

'No, no; please don't,' said Margaret anxiously.

'But my dear lady, don't you know that a large number of the men who have been East bring a boy back with them to this country?'

'Oh, you mean a servant?' said Margaret with sudden relief.

'Of course I do. Good night, you don't – yes, a servant, a boy.'

'Oh, yes, yes,' said Margaret. 'No, Claude didn't.'

'Ah. Then I don't suppose you've ever tasted decent curry,' said Mr Mock.

'I like this curry, I must admit.'

'Exactly,' grunted Mr Mock. 'Oh, what you miss! No decent curry. No real turtle. No Manila cigars under Heaven knows what price. No *goola Malacca*. Sometimes, by Jingo, I'm tempted to go back East.'

'I should yield to the temptation if I were you,' said Margaret.

That passing glimpse of solace which she had seen and lost awhile in the first brief moments of retreat on the terrace appeared not again. Just as her customary peace of mind seemed to be haunted by some shadowy apprehension which she could not shake off, so the soothing atmosphere of this dear old house was addled by the domination of this outrageous Mr Mock, disporting gloomily in its sacred shade, like a great ape violating a forsaken temple of prayer.

Mr Mock concluded his tiffin, stalked to the latticed window of the dining-room and surveyed the weather. It had improved. The rain storm had passed. A fitful glimmer of sunshine appeared and disappeared in the face of the sky line like a cynical grin. Mr Mock, too, had improved. He said so. He said he had improved to such an extent that he now intended to take the air, to ascertain the whereabouts of the shooting party, and, unless the distance was too great, possibly to join it. He invited Margaret to accompany him. She declined courteously.

So Mr Mock trudged forth alone. The sun began to shine more steadily upon the peaceful terrace. The gardener came forth and resumed his finicking occupation. Pansy frolicked coquettishly around the prone and forbearing spaniel. A whistling boy with a bicycle came up the drive and delivered a telegram.

Margaret took it from him. It was addressed to Lady Bunter. She weighed it for a moment between her finger and thumb, speculating upon the yellow envelope with distant eyes. Then, taking it indoors, she handed it to Francis, who thanked her and propped it up with a clothesbrush on the hall table.

People are almost as optimistic about missing a rainstorm as they are about missing death. Though the heavy shower which had passed had been threatening to begin at any moment during the morning, quite a large number of people were caught in it and got wet. Sir Stirling Bunter was one of this number. Lady Bunter, who had left the cottage of the wife of the gamekeeper just as the storm broke, but who did not turn back because she was not quite certain what time Sam wanted his guests to have their lunch, and was quite used to rain, so it didn't really matter, was another. The two neighbours of Sir Stirling who had joined the shoot were likewise very wet. Mr Goodie, who had been in a particularly exposed position, was practically liquid. A little circle of pools gathered around them as they assembled for lunch in the inadequate shelter of a coppice.

'This is rotten,' said Sir Stirling. 'Fanny, my dearie, you're frightfully wet. I vote we quit this.'

'I'm not a bit wet,' responded Lady Bunter. 'I had my Asquithcutum.'

'Ay!' cried Mr Goodie with a burst of unusual enthusiasm. 'That is a grand wudd for it, Lady Bunt'r. It's a jooke I should 'a liked to have oreeginated. The Asquithcutum – proof against all political storrms. Ay, that's grand.'

'Haven't I used the right word?' asked Lady Bunter timidly.

'Course you have,' said her husband. 'That'll do, Goodie.

To return to the subject, I say that you are wet, my dear, and must go back home.'

'No, I'm not; but I think we will go back home because you and the others will all get colds, and—'

'I shan't,' cried Sir Stirling. 'I'm as dry as a bone.'

'Oh, Sam dear! I can see the water running off you.'

'Only off my mackintosh. Look here, Fan. Do go home yourself.'

Lady Bunter deliberated for a moment.

'It's a pity to spoil your sport,' she began.

'Rotten day,' put in Sir Stirling. 'I'm sick of it already.'

'Then let's all go home,' said Lady Bunter triumphantly.

And other wayfarers were caught and drenched in the unsparing progress of that storm. It caught an aged rustic idling at the roadside and drove him over the bank into the plantation, grumbling in high-pitched expostulations as though of pain.

It did not wet Dann very severely. He was overtaken by the first downpour as he stood, his cap pushed back and his coat slung over the wing of his car, investigating the second collapse of his lamentable radiator. He quickly got inside the car and pulled up the windows; after which he sat patiently watching the rain, chewing a rather greasy thumb, and wondering aloud with much frankness of expression why such visitations invariably overtook him on the most isolated and unfrequented roads in the country.

It wetted Peter. Peter was almost too preoccupied to care. He was walking at full speed into Downblotton, mentally commandeering special trains, composing telegrams, rehearsing telephone messages.

The storm passed Bristol and swept eastwards before the Bones had gained that objective. Mr Bone had called attention to it. Mrs Bone had said that it was small wonder he wanted to change the subject under discussion, if it were only to talk about the weather.

In the same train, three carriages away, in that very smoking carriage which Mrs Bone had recommended to her husband for sitting, Claude Hackett heard the sudden lash of rain upon the windows, and glanced up from his monthly review with a quick frown.

One of the most likely people in the world to be caught and wetted by a rainstorm which he had thoroughly anticipated was Sloley-Jones. He happened, however, to have made Glastonbury before it broke; and passing quickly into the precincts of the inn, where he intended to redeem the loss of his egg, got only slightly wet.

One of the least likely people in the world to fall a victim to caprice, even the caprice of the weather, was Mrs Spoker. But, despite the employment of an umbrella of dimensions which suggested that it had been bred by golf out of perambulator, Mrs Spoker got a little damp. It was but seldom that she allowed herself the worldly relaxation of a few hours away from the *Stag and Hunt*. Today, as it chanced, she had handed the care of the bedridden lady, the keys of the office and the respectable reputation of her inn to the joint agency of Gladys and Alfred, the old man of the bar; and, accepting the offer of a lift in the waggonette of a passing farmer of proved reliability, had set forth to enjoy a midday meal with her old acquaintance, Mrs Wigger, of Downblotton; together with what that punctilious lady was wont to describe for purposes of invitation as 'a few verbal words.'

# CHAPTER XVII

## 'Well Singes Thu, Cuccu'

Mr Claude Hackett, having lunched in the train, took the first opportunity of proceeding by rail to Glastonbury. It was here that the hiatus, which made the morning journey from London to Rushcombe Fitz-Chartres so troublesome, occurred; and, as he had previously been led to expect, he had an hour and a half to put in before he could obtain the necessary connection.

Having checked these details and deposited his luggage at the station, he went forth into the town. He did not saunter. It was not the nature of Claude Hackett to saunter. In order to put in the time, he was going to look at ruins which, truth to tell, interested him very little indeed. But, since force of circumstances demanded, or practically demanded, that he should go and look at ruins, he went to look at the ruins by the most direct route and at a brisk pace.

On arriving at the ruins he looked at them for the space of at least three minutes. He then looked at his watch.

Time itself seemed to be infected by the immobile grandeur of those patriarchal pillars and walls, standing yet indifferent to the speed and clamour of a modern environment. Claude Hackett wrinkled his brow whimsically at the thought and, attempting to bestir his very inert sense of duty towards the ruins, decided to walk round them once and to view them casually from every aspect.

He turned a corner and halted. He found himself confronted by a strange group of objects.

Immediately in his path stood a motor-cycle, propped up on its stand. A few yards in front of the cycle, projecting from behind a buttress of the ruined wall, were black human hindquarters. Watching these hindquarters furtively, while with one foot he was attempting to kick back the stand of the cycle, was a small boy.

Claude Hackett realised without a moment's hesitation that this meant mischief; that the small boy was intent upon amusing himself at the expense of the hindquarters to the probable detriment of the motor-cycle. He therefore cried aloud in a stern voice:

'Now then! What are you up to there?'

The effect of this was that the small boy, profiting by a long course of study in the topographical possibilities, disappeared completely and instantaneously; while conversely, by a remarkably laboured procedure, the whole of Sloley-Jones disengaged itself from the buttress.

'What's the matter?' asked Sloley-Jones. 'I'm only investigating something. I'm sorry, but it's quite all right surely? Are you a curator?'

'No,' said Hackett. 'I—'

'I'm only investigating something,' said Sloley-Jones. 'Besides, if you're not a curator, was it really necessary to shout like that? I bumped my head. Rotten.'

'I wasn't shouting at you,' said Hackett. 'Is this your motor-cycle?'

'It is, but really I must say I don't see why you should ask. I don't wish to appear ratty about it, but was it necessary to shout like that? It isn't in your way, is it? There seems to be plenty of room to get past. I'm awfully sorry, but I really fail to see why I shouldn't leave my motor-bicycle there; especially as you say you are not a curator or anything.'

'Look here, sir,' said Hackett, 'if you will allow me to explain, perhaps I may succeed in mollifying your apparently somewhat ruffled feelings.'

'Oh, I beg your pardon. I don't wish to appear ratty in the least. Only you gave me an awful jump and I bumped my head.'

'If you want to know, there was a little urchin trying to kick your bicycle over, and I shouted at him.'

'Oh, I say, I'm most intensely sorry for what I said,' cried Sloley-Jones. 'You must forgive me. I had no idea of course. To be startled and to bump one's head like that makes one a little impetuous. Thanks most awfully for looking after my bicycle.'

He advanced into the sunshine and tested the equilibrium of the cycle on its stand with a hand begrimed with his investigations.

He sought Claude Hackett's face and gave vent to a brief apologetic laugh on a single note. Hackett merely nodded. His long white face displayed no indication of amusement.

'I seem to have saved your cycle a bump at the expense of your head,' he observed.

'Oh, it's quite all right now – absolutely. Where did the boy go? Was it a boy?'

Hackett nodded.

'You said an urchin,' said Sloley-Jones, smiling. 'If the word urchin cannot be used in the feminine it ought to be able to be. Ha!'

'This was a boy,' said Hackett. 'He ran away when I shouted.'

'Very wise of him,' said Sloley-Jones loudly, as though to warn the boy against further activities should he have been listening, which he was. 'They ought not to allow these wretched children to come playing about here. They are a perpetual nuisance – unspeakable. They deface the beauties of the walls and molest people who take an intelligent interest. I should like to take it up with the curators. In my opinion it is nothing short of desecration. Don't you think so?'

The question was rhetorical. The bump which the parson's head had received was not so great a shock as was the brisk manner in which the stranger took up the unintentional challenge.

'No,' said Hackett. 'Since you ask, I can't say that I agree with you.'

The discomfited Sloley-Jones gazed in great surprise at

the well-dressed, gentle-mannered stranger who thus unhesitatingly proclaimed himself a champion of the Goths.

'No? Really? You – you surprise me, I must say. Surely you agree that it is a pity that a magnificent old – pile – edifice like this should become a – a playground for people with no veneration? Oh, it's awful. Do you know that a woman named Bertha Harris has actually had the indecency to carve her name with a penknife on that buttress? If people are Vandals and Yahoos they might surely stay away. Why should anybody be allowed here who has no respect for remains, which are without parallel, remember? You can't replace them when Bertha Harris and other slubberdegullions have done their work. I would have no one near the place who was not prepared to do it honour.'

The parson spoke not without heat, but with due intent to exercise gentle persuasion upon his puzzling interlocutor.

Claude Hackett raised his head deliberately and gazed at the outraged buttress with the eyes of a cynic.

'I am not prepared to honour it, I am afraid,' he said in his well-modulated, rather nasal voice.

He seemed about to say more but forbore. Sloley-Jones could only scratch the bridge of his nose and feel at singular loss for words.

Hackett's eyes returned slowly to the round, inquisitive spectacles. A smile, which was more like the promise of a smile unfulfilled, flickered over his keen countenance.

'No,' he said, as though continuing an argument. 'There are some temples which can never be defaced, far less destroyed; but they are temples not built with hands. Temples of Science, temples of Literature, where the worshippers may gain knowledge and refreshment in the pursuit of knowledge. Those are the temples which I would have held sacred. As for an old church' – he waved his hand expressively towards the ruin – 'what's the good of it? Bertha Harris is of far greater importance to me than the stone she cut her name on.'

Sloley-Jones had opened his mouth half an inch but made

no reply. He looked with increasing interest at the tall, commanding man who stood before him. The face was so long and thin as to suggest that in his infancy it had been caught and squeezed like a lemon, but the prevailing expression emphasised by the clean-cut, pointed chin seemed to imply tenacity rather than resolve. The eyes, deeply set, were kind and forbearing, in direct contrast to the austerity of mouth and chin. For the rest Sloley-Jones noticed shamefacedly that the stranger was undoubtedly a man of unusually cleanly habits. His hands and linen were spotless. He was clothed quietly but with a finish. He was certainly the last man whom one could expect to find engaged upon an occupation which he confessed was objectionable, and defying harmless tourists whose only desire was to investigate piously and in peace.

This thought seemed to occur to the stranger too. There was an apologetic note in his voice as he continued:

'I don't wish to inflict my views upon you. Every one is entitled to his own.'

'Oh, that's all right – quite. I like it,' said Sloley-Jones.

'I am afraid I took you up rather briskly,' said Hackett. 'I should like to make my meaning clear if I can.'

'Oh, do. I say. This is quite interesting. Well?'

'I see you are a clergyman. Those who profess to have any respect for the clergy are usually apt to proceed to the other extreme and allow their precepts to pass unchallenged.'

Sloley-Jones repeated his one-note laugh.

'On the good old principle of casting the first stone, perhaps,' he remarked. 'Don't mind me. Go on. I like this.'

'I should have thought,' said Hackett gently, 'that the worship which you appear to devote to a mere pile of stones was hard to reconcile with your spiritual principles. It is the work of men's hands; and whether it is a piece of antique masonry or a golden calf appears to me to be immaterial. That, however, is beside the point.'

'One half tick,' cried Sloley-Jones. 'By Jove, this is splendid. I can see I'm going to have a perfectly topping argument with you. But first of all, aren't your own spiritual principles the same as my own, may I ask?'

'I should think it is very unlikely,' said Hackett.

'You are a Christian?'

'Certainly.'

'Church of England?'

'Yes.'

'Well then. If I may say so, you are hardly the sort of person whom one usually finds oneself up against; the sort of person who seems to find a wretched form of amusement in going about cheeking the Church. You have already associated yourself with Bertha Harris. You now seem to be on the point of joining forces with the bicycle urchin.'

Sloley-Jones grinned broadly with the joy of controversy and rubbed his hands.

'Yes,' replied Hackett. 'If I had known that you, a clergyman of the Church of England, were really prodding about behind that wall from a sense of duty, I think I should have felt rather inclined to kick your bicycle over myself, as a mild form of active protest.'

'Isn't this too priceless?' was Sloley-Jones's comment. 'Now, what's your point?'

'Well, very briefly, this. All around you' – Hackett waved a white, comprehensive hand – 'while you employ your energetic piety upon this buttress, there is raging a continual battle. The battle against poverty and' – he twisted his mouth sardonically – 'other forms of sin.'

'I know,' cried the parson. 'You needn't tell me that. I don't shirk the battle, believe me. This is my relaxation.'

'But the forces opposed to you in the battle are without exception the first-fruits of this archaism which you pause to admire; doctrines and heresies and prejudices as obsolete as these walls. The only difference between them is that this is a helpless ruin; they are the opposite extreme. They are a prison.'

'Antiquity' – he raised his voice as Sloley-Jones showed signs of interrupting – 'is no blessing to us. It is a curse which should be rooted out of every present-day calculation. The only relics we should venerate are those I spoke of – the records of Science and Literature. In other respects custom and dogma are as great a curse as the diseases which still survive from previous generations to poison our own.'

'By Jove,' said Sloley-Jones, 'I believe you are a Socialist.'

'Oh yes,' agreed the other readily. 'Though that is a term which is abused as a political label.'

'Abused? I should have thought that the most violent section of the Labour Party would have been too tame for you.'

Hackett shook his head with one of his brief, fluttering smiles.

'I deprecate violence,' he said.

'Anyhow,' said Sloley-Jones, 'I should put you down as an advanced Liberal.'

'Not advanced,' was the reply. 'Some of the old party who thought more of their prize than their creed have advanced. Some have retired. True Liberals have done neither. I have done neither.'

'Ah,' said Sloley-Jones. 'You know I'm awfully glad we met – uncommon glad. Of course I can't take an active part in politics; but I'm frightfully keen on the subject – keen as mustard. Personally I'm an old-fashioned, full-out, die-hard Imperialist Tory of the most bigoted and relentless type; so we could have a simply topping debate. But I dare say you haven't time.'

'Oh, my dear padre,' said Hackett in a tone which appeared almost light-hearted in comparison with his former zeal, 'I really don't wish to inflict my views upon you. You mustn't think that I attack every stranger I meet in this manner. Circumstances seem to have thrown us into contention.'

'Not at all,' said Sloley-Jones. 'I really am awfully glad we struck each other. I don't suppose it's any use our trying to convert each other. But one doesn't often get the chance of a discussion with a really genuine Liberal nowadays.'

'Ah, I think the wish is father to that thought,' said Hackett. 'The race is by no means extinct, I assure you.'

Sloley-Jones adjusted his spectacles and beamed past the face of his disputant, gleefully preparing his master-stroke.

'I suppose,' he said, 'that you wouldn't believe me if I were to tell you that the Free Liberal party in the House of Commons is simply sitting on the fence waiting to see which way the cat is going to jump?'

'No,' said Hackett cordially. 'I shouldn't.'

'I'm really sorry for you fellows,' went on Sloley-Jones. 'There must be quite a large number of you who are genuinely consistent to your creed; but you can have no idea how you are being hoodwinked by your members and leaders.'

'Really?' observed the other darkly. 'This is very interesting. I can't say that I was aware of this spiritual wickedness in high places.'

'No,' said Sloley-Jones, pursing up his lips and assuming a very matter-of-fact tone, 'I don't suppose you are. I only happen to know what I am talking about because I had it straight from the horse's mouth only last night. I was talking to a friend of mine, who is himself a Free Liberal member, and he told me quite openly and without any compunction that the whole bunch of them are simply waiting to sell themselves to the highest bidder.'

'Indeed?' said Hackett with honest surprise. 'I happen to know one or two of the party members. Who, may I ask, was this rather outspoken friend of yours?'

'Oh, I don't want to give him away,' said Sloley-Jones quickly. 'I might damage his reputation in the party. For all I know you may be a member of the House yourself.'

'Yes, I am,' said Hackett.

'Oh dear,' exclaimed the parson. 'Then I – I don't think I ought to say more.'

'Are you sure you ought to have said as much?'

'What?'

'Please don't be offended; but doesn't it strike you that

this anonymous reactionary of yours is rather the sort of figure that one connects with underhand election methods?'

'Oh, come! You must take my word for it that I really did have the conversation.'

'I don't doubt it for a moment, if you say so. But the gentleman in question must have been a greater friend of yours than he is of his party.'

'No, as a matter of fact,' burst out Sloley-Jones, 'I expect you honestly take your politics a sight more seriously than the majority. This was really the first time I had ever met this man, though I have known his wife for years. He was stopping with his wife last night at an inn not far from here, and I happened to call in and find them there and the wife introduced me to him. He was perfectly frank and open about his politics from the first. Of course he said he shouldn't care to repeat all he told me from his seat in the House; but I gained the impression that he was heartily sick of the entire outfit.'

'Oh well,' said Hackett, the light of solution appearing to dawn upon his perplexed features, 'I needn't encroach further on your confidences. I know the man you mean. He's going to resign almost directly.'

'He didn't tell me that,' said Sloley-Jones, sinking his voice unconsciously in intimate curiosity. 'That's queer – extraordinary. His wife would have told me anyhow I should have thought.'

'You are speaking of Bruce Gladwin, are you not?'

'No. Well, don't let it go any further, but I am speaking of a man called Hackett.'

Claude Hackett was carrying a straight walking-stick of handsome snake-wood. He leant forward, with both hands upon the heavy gold knob which surmounted it and executed a little pirouetting half-turn with his weight on the stick. When he raised his head his tongue was stuck in his cheek, which gave a singular expression of masterful irony to his long grave face.

'I'm very much afraid, padre,' he said, 'that you have been imposed upon in this matter. I have my own reasons for saying that the man you conversed with last night could not possibly have been Hackett.'

'Oh, but you're wrong, excuse me. You're absolutely out. I saw both—'

'Why he should have represented himself as Hackett I have no idea but I do happen to know that Hackett was in London last night.'

'Oh no, look here, you can't pass it off like that,' said Sloley-Jones, smiling still but showing some evidence of resentment in his voice. 'I tell you the man was there with his wife. I have known his wife for years. She was Margaret Bliss – you know, the Margaret Bliss Home for Children – and—'

'Yes, that's right,' assented the other sharply. 'She married Hackett. Well?'

'I say, she was there with her husband. She introduced me to him. They were motoring and had got stranded. I found them at this inn at a place called Maiden Blotton, a village about three miles from here. They stayed there last night and went on this morning to the Bunters' place at Rushcombe. So you see I know my facts.'

He paused with a long and triumphant intake of the breath. That he had gained his point was obvious from the baffled expression of his disputant. He saw the keen eyes narrowed as though the possessor were making a mental calculation.

Sloley-Jones was not the man to miss driving his advantage home. The point under discussion seemed to his energetic mind to be of intrinsic value to the political argument. He held a Liberal M.P. flabbergasted in debate. It was delicious. He sailed hotly in to complete the rout.

'You say you know Mrs Hackett,' he said. 'If you know her as well as I do, you will realise that she is not the sort of woman to pretend that a man is her husband when he is not, just for a joke.'

'No, no. I quite agree with you there,' acknowledged Hackett. 'Mrs Hackett is a very honourable and a very irreproachable woman in every way.'

'I'm glad to hear you say so,' said Sloley-Jones. 'I have always said so too. There was some mischievous scandal about her at one time. Jealousy, I expect. Disgusting! That was really why she started all her philanthropic work. They say she would never have married Hackett if she hadn't meant to chuck her own society crowd. However, I was very agreeably surprised with Hackett. I had always been given to understand the man was rather an ass.'

The other tapped his toe impatiently with his stick and glanced around him quickly. He seemed to be in two minds. Sloley-Jones was delighted with his success. He had this rooted Liberal by the hip, he felt, on any subject.

'If you still feel any doubt in your mind about what I have told you,' he said casually, 'I can soon disprove it quite finally. The Hacketts remained at the inn for the night. In the middle of the night Hackett got out of bed and went down to let out their dog which was howling, and lost it. As a matter of fact I found the dog this morning and returned it to them. The landlady of the inn was disturbed by queer noises in the night – probably caused by the dog – and went down to their room and found them both asleep together in bed. So there you are. We both know Mrs Hackett well enough to let it stand at that; though I fancy one of us must know the husband rather better than the other does.'

Chortling over which sarcasm Sloley-Jones turned rapturously to his bicycle.

Hackett's eyes were wide open now, but they had lost all their forbearance. His brows were knitted. The drawn austere face displayed no sign of anger. For a moment there passed over it that shadow of a smile, as though in answer to one merry little thought struggling in the complexity of his mind. He made a sudden movement with his hand as though to regain the parson's attention; then thought better of it and brought the hand slowly back to the knob of his stick.

He stood watching Sloley-Jones's fidgety attentions to his bicycle with an abstracted stare, as the idler of a harbour town watches a ship at sea.

He drew himself up and threw back his shoulders.

'I think it's time that I was making a move,' he said.

'A – h!' responded Sloley-Jones, glancing up from the bicycle. 'Well, we haven't had much of a debate after all – pity!'

Hackett nodded pleasantly and turned, swinging his stick.

'And, I say,' added Sloley-Jones mischievously, 'don't split on me to Hackett. And, I say, don't take your politics too seriously. Nobody else does. Cheero.'

Round the corner whence he had come first upon the bicycle, the urchin, the hindquarters, Hackett paused and apostrophised the ruined walls in a sinister whisper.

'Do I dream?' he said.

Then he walked at top speed to the nearest garage. He did not pause to ask his way. He seemed instinctively to discern the shortest route.

Ten minutes later Sloley-Jones was just in time to see him depart with his luggage from the station. He had chartered a local car. Sloley-Jones knew that car.

The parson dismounted and watched the car curiously as it sped out of the town. He turned to the porter who had been assisting at its loading and who was now standing and indolently whistling as he fingered his largess.

'I say,' said Sloley-Jones. 'Do you happen to know who that gentleman is?'

The porter, who apparently valued his music above his manners, shook his head without ceasing to whistle.

'Didn't you notice his name on the labels of his luggage or anything?'

The porter shook his head in a manner which only served to emphasise the high note which he had achieved at this moment.

'Do you happen to know where he is off to?' insisted Sloley-Jones.

The porter frowned, ejaculated 'Main Blon, I believe,' and continued whistling.

'Maid-en B-lotton?' repeated Sloley-Jones suspiciously.

The porter nodded almost imperceptibly, dug his hands into his trouser pockets, turned towards the station doorway and took a flying kick at a piece of waste paper in his path, all without the loss of a note.

'How awfully rum,' murmured Sloley-Jones aloud. 'What's his game? Dash! This is awfully rum.'

He mounted his cycle deliberately. There was a back-fire like a revolver shot and the porter, turning his head quickly, was gassed out of tune by superfluous lubrication, as Sloley-Jones commenced his pursuit of the mysteriously inquisitive Liberal M.P. in the car.

# CHAPTER XVIII

## 'Pass, Friend'

Peter, his light overcoat buttoned haphazard over his shoulders and distorting his whole appearance, entered the Downblotton post office in a manner so violent that the postmaster thought he was being held up by a bandit. When he recognised the young man who had been in the company of the interrogative lady with furs and the red-moustached chauffeur that morning, his hostility became, if anything, intensified.

'I've got to get through to London quickly,' cried Peter. 'How long does it take?'

The postmaster removed a worn portfolio containing stamps from the counter and placed it in a drawer. He tried to close the drawer which was ill-fitting and stuck. He pulled the drawer open again and repeated the experiment. Again it stuck. He pulled the drawer completely out of its seating, which he examined minutely, stooping with his aged head on a level with the counter. He then blew into the seating and attempted to replace the drawer. After two or three efforts he succeeded in wedging the drawer into its aperture. Exerting considerable energy he pushed it home. He then pulled it out again to see whether he had jammed it. He had jammed it. Finally he managed to pull it out again and to push it in again two or three times without a jam. He then removed the stamp portfolio from the drawer and replaced it on the counter. He turned a very inhospitable scowl in Peter's direction and said:

'How?'

'Yes, how long?' repeated Peter, who was lathering his perspiring brow with a coloured silk handkerchief.

'How long how?' said the postmaster.

'By telephoning of course. How do you imagine I want to get through to London? Do you think I want to bore a tunnel there or something? Come on; shake a leg for Heaven's sake. I'm in a hurry.'

The postmaster rearranged the position of the portfolio upon the counter.

'How long do it take to get through to London by telephone?' he declaimed.

'Yes,' said Peter. 'How long to London by telephone. There can have been nothing like you since the days of Moore and Burgess.'

'Well, 'ow can I tell 'ow long it may take?' said the postmaster. 'Sometimes it takes a great deal longer to get through to London from 'ere than at other times by a lot. Other times it don't take so long not to get through than you might expect by quite a time.'

'Where do I speak from?' said Peter quickly.

'If folks comes in 'ere and says "'ow long does it take to get through to London?" 'ow can I say 'ow long it may take?' grumbled the postmaster. 'There's more—'

Peter was already in the telephone box, having at length discovered its whereabouts by his own observation.

He was intensely worried; but, to do him justice, it was the fear that Sophia had undergone an ordeal of weariness and depression by reason of his own neglect which distressed him far more than the prospect of retribution. The knowledge that he would never be able to make Sophia believe this did not detract from his agitation.

He decided that he would remain in that telephone box until he succeeded in communicating with the flat. It was not a pleasing prospect, for the box was very close and rancid with the long imprisoned fumes of cheap tobacco. But Peter could not face a long vigil in the company of the postmaster. In his present state of mind he might be driven to kill the postmaster, which would only add to the already sufficient complications in which he was involved.

Resolutely curbing his impatience, he engaged in nego-

tiations with a succession of female voices which sounded
like the efforts of aspirants for the part of the canary in a
Maeterlinck fantasy. The drums of his ears were assaulted
with frequent but unexpected detonations of the most rend-
ing and horrisonous description. He overheard fevered con-
versations, now rising to a bellow, now fading to a distant
screech of endeavour, as though the principals were straining every nerve to allow him to eavesdrop. Another bom-
bardment would follow; then the chirrup of one of the
canaries, blissfully greeting the lull after a thunderstorm. He
breathed back fervent directions and imprecations into a receiver around which the stale tobacco fumes seemed to have
concentrated in an almost visible integument of glutinous
substance.

For how long he remained in that telephone box, Peter
never knew. For how long he implored, resisted, argued, he
lost all reckoning. His most trying altercation was with a
voice which claimed to belong to 'trunk supervisor', which
sinister title seemed appropriate to a vulture rather than a
canary, though the voice yielded to none in its qualities of
chirrup. Fortunately, just as Peter was losing his temper with
the trunk supervisor, a motor-bus with a missing engine apparently took up its position between them; and by the time
this moved on the supervisor had departed and had been
succeeded by a breezy gentleman who asked Peter
confidently whether he was Mrs Rowbottom.

At the end of twenty-three minutes there quavered in
Peter's ears, out of the chaos of earthquake, fire and thunder,
the shrill but distant echoes of a still, small voice. He recognised with amazement, unable to avoid the impression that
they reached him only by some superhuman coincidence, the
accents of the bitter housemaid, Tessie, of his London flat.
Even then he was assailed by an over-exacting canary, who
interrupted the first outpourings of his inquiries to ask him
whether he was speaking.

The charity that thinketh no evil cannot be cited as one of
Tessie's most luminous characteristics. She had views as to

the most probable course of Peter's procedure during the last few hours beside which Mrs Bone's assumptions were sunny optimism. Tessie had certainly never anticipated this glorious opportunity of contributing her quota to the miscreant's discomfiture. She made the most of it.

Without venturing to state her own feelings in the matter, she gave Peter a vivid impression of the reckoning awaiting him. She described the return of the forlorn and weary Sophia, the advent of Mrs Bone, the investigations and discoveries of that matron, the final vigorous swoop of the entire family, refreshed by enlightenment and unremitting in vengeance, upon his inadequate refuge in the by-ways of Somerset. Ten thousand miles of telephone line could not have modulated the ring of virulent triumph in Tessie's voice, as she greeted Peter with these galling facts.

How had Mrs Bone discovered where he was? Ah. *She* found out, never fear. Tessie lingered over the point with an underlying hint of reproach that Peter should ever have issued such a challenge to that master intelligence. At length she disclosed the means whereby Mrs Bone had achieved this *coup*.

Peter rang off. He burst from the telephone box, threw a florin at the postmaster and ran out into the street, deaf to the flood of squeaky protestation which followed him. He passed rapidly up and down the street in anxious search for any evidences of a garage. He escaped collision with a butcher's cart by a hair's breadth. He participated, under protest, in the struggles of some small boys who were inaugurating the football season. Presently, more by luck than good management, he discovered the local policeman.

No, there was no garage in Downblotton and a good job too. Was there a cycle-shop? Yes, there was a cycle-shop. Where? There. Peter dashed on.

He was in no mind for haggling. He was as clay in the hands of the cycle dealer, who invented record terms for the loan of a bicycle with a saddle which might have been inven-

ted as a mild mediaeval torture. The dealer could have sold
Peter the bicycle had he known.

Peter paid in advance and sped away. The bicycle emitted
a strange protesting groan at every circuit of the chain. He
paid small heed. He was as hungry and nearly as weary as on
the last occasion when he sought the *Stag and Hunt*. But
every other consideration gave place to the frenzied hope of
short-circuiting the retributive Mrs Bone ere she held him,
forsworn and abject, in the meshes of her net.

If only he could see Sophia first, could explain; failing
explanation, could plead. It would be obvious to her that his
love was genuine and immutable. Peter pushed on,
indifferent to the galling saddle, indifferent to the faintness
of hunger; seeing only the relentless vision of Mrs Bone
mounting the staircase of the *Stag and Hunt* to view the
bedroom, having completed her grim investigations of the
office register.

He plied the pedals to the limit of exertion, freewheeling
occasionally only as a means to gather strength for a further
onslaught. Fortunately the road was clear. It was a narrow
road and muddy, but there was no traffic to impede his progress. The female figure hastening towards him was the first
he had encountered since leaving Downblotton.

The female in question, who had been hurrying, halted on
seeing the bicycle and remained in a huddled attitude at the
extreme edge of the road, apparently under the impression
that this was the only means whereby she could avoid being
knocked down by any passing vehicle. Peter, straining ahead,
glanced at the female as he passed. He recognised her face.
More, her face bore some subtle connection to all the tumult
of fear and misfortune which possessed his thoughts.

He slackened his pace and turned in his saddle before he
actually identified the face. The female was standing
gazing after him. Peter stopped.

'Hallo!' he cried. 'It's – what's-your-name.'

The female, who was out of breath, responded with an
ingurgitation of assent.

'Yes, that's right,' said Peter, returning towards her. 'The *Stag* girl.'

The female's appearance was hardly in keeping with this rather pastoral description. She nodded and snorted her assent in a manner which suggested that the 'Girl-stag' would have been more appropriate.

'Gladys, isn't it?' continued Peter.

Gladys snorted and nodded.

'Where are you off to?'

'Downbl—' replied Gladys, catching her breath at the second syllable and completing her information with a demonstrative thumb.

'Downblotton? Why? Tell me, what has happened at the pub – the inn – Stag – Hunt?'

'Goin' – ter get – Mrs Spo – ker, I am,' said Gladys.

'Mrs Spoker? Why, is she in Downblotton?'

Gladys nodded and snorted.

'Good,' murmured Peter. 'But why get her? What's up?'

The old lady, Gladys explained with much difficulty, had told her to go into Downblotton as quick as she could and bring Mrs Spoker back at once.

'The old lady?' Peter turned and scanned the road before him with haunted eyes.

Gladys nodded several times.

'Damn!' whispered Peter.

'What is this old lady doing? Where is she now?'

'In the bedroom,' said Gladys.

'Oh, my God!' said Peter. 'Why does she want Mrs Spoker? Look here, Gladys. It's no good your going and getting Mrs Spoker. I'm on my way to the *Stag* now and I'll see the old lady and tell her all she wants to know.'

There was little room in Gladys's face for any signs but those of heat and bronchial distress. Peter's offer brought only a glimmer of mild surprise to her expression. She shook her head.

'I 'ave to get Mrs Spoker,' she affirmed. 'The old – lady

was in a terrible – state when she 'eared as 'ow – Mrs Spoker
wasn – ther. She's very sick I reckon.'

'I reckon she is,' agreed Peter. 'But, look here, Gladys, I
know what I'm talking about. If that old lady saw Mrs
Spoker she'd only go and get Mrs Spoker into great trouble.
I know what she's after. You simply must not go and get Mrs
Spoker. It's a most extraordinarily lucky thing that Mrs
Spoker isn't there.'

'I 'ave to,' insisted Gladys. 'The old – lady may be goin' ter
die for all what – I know. She looks – 'orrible.'

'Die, nonsense! Why should she die? I wish – well,
anyhow, she always looks like that.'

'She don't, I don't think,' said Gladys. 'She's mutterin'
awful and 'er eyes is all rollin'.'

'Good Lord, she must have worked herself into a state,'
reflected Peter disconsolately. 'Did she ask you many questions?'

'Not many,' said Gladys. 'She jest says, "Wher's the
lan'lady? What do she mean by bein' out when I – most
wants 'er?" she says. "Go and get 'er – back this minute," she
says.'

Peter nodded gloomily.

'I know,' he said. 'You give quite a vivid impression of her,
Gladys. I can imagine exactly.'

'Yes,' said Gladys with smouldering resentment. 'She was
like that from the moment she first come.'

'Yes, and a good while before that if you only knew,' said
Peter. 'But you needn't think she's ill. She's always like that.'

'No, she is ill, I'm sure o' that,' said Gladys. 'From the look
of 'er she may easy be goin' ter die.'

'Oh, don't go on talking in that ridiculous way,' said Peter
irritably. 'Why on earth should she die?'

'She'll 'ave ter die sometime,' replied Gladys with a shrug.

'Yes, I suppose so, with luck,' said Peter. 'But you needn't
think she's going to lie down and die on this particular afternoon, because flukes like that only happen in books for very
small boys.'

'I 'ave ter get a doctor to 'er anyway,' said Gladys pertinently.

'A doctor? Who says so?'

'She did.'

'She said she wanted to have a doctor? Then she really has been taken worse. This is more interesting. What's the matter with her? What are her symptoms like?'

'She didn't show 'em to me,' said Gladys.

'But was she ill when she arrived? By the way, I suppose the others were with her? A gentleman with a moustache and a lady?'

'No, she come by herself and she 'as bin by herself all the time. Gave it out she 'ad no friends,' said Gladys.

'I should think she might be quite right about that,' said Peter. 'But are you sure her husband wasn't with her?'

'No,' said Gladys emphatically. 'Nobody.'

'And her daughter; her daughter's my – h'm, yes. Well, when did she come; at what time?'

'At what time o' day?' said Gladys opening her mouth and assuming a reminiscential air.

'Yes.'

'About six-thirty, I think it would be.'

'Oh, look here, don't be ridiculous, Gladys. I'm only trying to help you with this old lady. What time did she arrive at the pub? Now think.'

'I can't rightly remember,' said Gladys. 'It wer' three weeks ago or more.'

'Three wee—' Peter wheeled upon her with a suddenness which frightened Gladys not a little. 'What old lady are you talking about?' he cried.

'The old lady above the bar,' gasped Gladys.

'Oh, thank Heaven!' said Peter. 'So all that has happened is that the old lady above the bar has been suddenly taken ill? Is that it?'

'Yes,' said Gladys.

'Oh, thank Heaven,' repeated Peter fervently. 'That's splendid. Then nobody else has turned up at the *Stag*?'

The startled Gladys could only display her tongue and shake her head again.

'Good!' exclaimed Peter springing on to his bicycle. 'Now, don't you go and frighten Mrs Spoker. She needn't hurry back. The old lady probably grudges her an afternoon off. Tell Mrs Spoker that. Say it will be all right if Mrs Spoker strolls home in the cool of the evening.'

The instructions were rather lost on Gladys, who had already been walking for an hour and was prepared to continue her journey without respite. She was fully convinced in her own mind that the spirit of the old lady would inevitably pass that evening, unless Mrs Spoker could be summoned in time to forbid it to pass; in which case, as Gladys knew from experience, it would have to be a very bold spirit indeed if it still insisted on passing. Unless, however, she used her best endeavour to secure Mrs Spoker, the spirit might pass before that lady had obtained a chance of checking it; in which case Gladys would be a murderess and have her photograph in the *News of the World*. Gladys therefore watched Peter out of sight curiously; then, summoning her energies, hastened forward to Downblotton.

'It might be worse,' thought Peter, as he pedalled on in the opposite direction. 'Nobody's shown up so far. Mrs Spoker isn't there. Gladys isn't there. I may be able to get there first and see how the land lies. As long as I can keep it dark about that damned bed, I ought to be able to pull off the reconciliation stunt. If only I can clear them out before Mrs Spoker gets back. Just my luck if that blinking incumbent had run into them and worked up some more of his priestcraft. Still, at the moment, it does look as if it might be worse.'

His feet kept pace with his busy mind. He ploughed onward along the heavy road for five and twenty minutes; at the end of which he was rewarded by a distant prospect of the *Stag and Hunt*, standing, deserted and at peace, in the afternoon sunshine.

# CHAPTER XIX

## Alfred and the Shining Hour

Peter opened the inn door cautiously and peered inside. There was no sign of life. He waited in the hall for a moment irresolutely, then ascended the stairs. From the bedroom above the bar echoed a distant wheezing sound. Otherwise all was still.

Peter returned to the hall, pushed open the door which led to the bar and entered. Old Alfred was reclining in a semi-comatose state in a cottage chair. His head was resting against the fireplace. He struggled with a grunt of surprise into a sitting posture.

He recognised Peter with a sleepy nod. The latter had recruited the services of Alfred that morning in the search for Pansy, and, fortunately, had rewarded him extremely handsomely for doing nothing and doing it very slowly.

'I've come back, Alfred,' Peter announced. 'There are some people coming to see me here this afternoon, but you needn't disturb yourself in any way. If they want anything I'll tell you. I've seen Gladys and know all about everything. I haven't had any lunch. I should like a sandwich and some beers.'

'Ah, ye can't get nothing to eat out o' me, sir,' said Alfred. 'It's too late. As fer beer, it's too late for that too be rights.'

'Rights, Alfred? What are rights?'

'Wrongs mostly,' replied Alfred philosophically. 'Well, if ye don't say nothing I'll give ye some beer, sir.'

'That's the spirit,' said Peter. 'You may as well be thoroughly independent while you are about it and give me quite a lot of beer. Join me, Alfred, join me. Let us drown rights.'

Alfred effected the preparations for this programme with

furtive zest. He also found some antique biscuits. Within two minutes Peter was feeling in better fettle for the reception of Mrs Bone.

'Now, look here, Alfred,' he proceeded, as he refreshed himself, 'let me give you a word of warning against these people who are coming here this afternoon. They are up to no good. They are trying to make mischief about me and about the *Stag*. We don't want Mrs Spoker to lose her licence. By the way, here's another five shillings for you, Alfred. Now, if these people ask you any questions, you just pretend not to know anything at all.'

'Anything about what?' asked Alfred, rubbing the tip of his nose with his pewter pot in a mystified manner.

'Anything about anything,' said Peter.

'Well, I don't,' said Alfred.

'Good,' said Peter. 'The best thing you can really do is to have another beer and go to sleep quietly in here.'

'Oh, I got to look arter the place, sir,' said Alfred, 'or ye never know what might not 'appen. Still, ther' might be something in what you say about 'aving another. Funny about me, I allus gets thirsty arter rain.'

'Right,' said Peter. 'You carry on, Alfred. You'll be all right. The weather hasn't settled yet.'

He placed his pewter upon the bar counter as he spoke and, raising his head, listened intently. From without came the unmistakable sounds of a car approaching and slackening speed. The moment had arrived.

'These will be the people,' he said quickly. 'Remember what I say, Alfred. Don't even see them if you can help it, and, if you can't, pretend to know absolutely damn all.'

'About what?' asked Alfred insistently.

'Pretend to be a perfect silly fool,' said Peter.

'Oh, I can't do that,' said Alfred. 'It ain't natural.'

'Oh well, I dare say it will be quite all right if you can be natural,' said Peter.

He closed the bar door behind him quietly. The hall door had not yet been opened from outside. Peter crossed the hall and entered the parlour. Creeping eagerly to the window he held the curtain a little on one side and peeped out.

A tall, spare man turned from issuing directions to his chauffeur, who touched his cap, operated his side break and stretched himself. The tall man swept the exterior of the *Stag* with a cursory glance and stepped rapidly towards the door.

Peter released the curtain.

'The doctor,' he reflected. 'Dash it, I never thought he would turn up so soon. This may complicate things.'

He assumed a careless attitude upon the hearthrug of the parlour and waited. He heard the inn door opened and closed; a firm step in the passage. It passed the parlour and proceeded towards the office. After a moment it returned. The parlour door was pushed open rather roughly.

'Oh,' said Hackett.

His manner had the troubled preoccupation of a slow man in a hurry.

'Oh, good afternoon,' said Peter.

'Can you tell me where I can find the landlord?'

'Yes, there isn't one,' said Peter pleasantly. 'There's only a landlady and she's out. You're the doctor, aren't you? The old lady you've come to see is upstairs in bed. You can't mistake the way, because there are only two bedrooms. Hers is the one above the bar.'

Despite his hurry Claude Hackett allowed him to complete these unnecessary instructions. It was a habit of his to hear all that another had to say to him. Peter met the kindly eyes with a discomforting sensation that he was being searched.

'I am sorry,' said Hackett, 'to disappoint the old lady in question. I am not the doctor.'

'Oh, I beg your pardon,' murmured Peter hastily.

'You are a guest here no doubt? I—'

'No,' said Peter. 'Oh no, I – I merely just happen to be – to be here, as it were, at the moment; don't you know?'

'I wonder,' continued Hackett, waiting again for this explanation in full, 'whether you could be so kind as to inform me where I can find somebody who represents the management of this establishment. I fail to see any signs of activity outside.'

Peter chortled agreeably. 'If you wait for another quarter of an hour, my boy,' he was thinking, 'you'll see all the activity you want.'

'The landlady,' he explained aloud, 'has gone off into Downblotton apparently for an afternoon on the buzz. I told you about the old lady above the bar. Well, she's been laid up here for weeks and has of course been taken ill at the most inconvenient moment; so the inn maid, Gladys, has also pushed off to Downblotton after the landlady and a doctor. That's why I thought you were the doctor.'

Hackett nodded gravely.

'And are the landlady and Gladys the sole custodians of the premises?'

'Yes,' replied Peter. 'At least, there is an additional old man to be found somewhere in the depths of the bar, but I'm afraid he is *non* pretty well *compos mentis*, as they say.'

'I dare say he will serve my purpose. Thank you,' said Claude Hackett, turning towards the door.

'I'm afraid he won't you know,' said Peter, restlessly preparing to follow. 'If you will allow me—'

Hackett paused. His face had grown slightly sterner.

'I know pretty well all there is to know about this pub,' continued Peter. 'If there's anything I can do for you—'

'No thank you,' said Hackett politely. 'I called in to make some private inquiries. Which is the bar, please?'

Peter indicated the opposite door with a somewhat grudging finger.

'There you are,' he said. 'You mustn't mind my saying so, but really making private inquiries of Alfred is one of the most piffling occupations one could possibly choose. However, you'll discover that for yourself. If I can assist you in any way, I shall be in the parlour.'

Mr Hackett's face showed no resentment at this gratuitous

comment. He entered the bar. Peter returned to the parlour with a shadow of unwelcome suspicion on his brow.

'Private inquiries?' A sinister mission for this sinister man to undertake. What private inquires could he have to make at the *Stag*, and who had sent him to make them? A solicitor, was he? No, Peter told himself, he would be a very unusual solicitor. Solicitors were men with moustaches, which got wet when they drank tea, and curious trousers. His father-in-law might easily have been a solicitor. This man looked more like a barrister. Or a detective. A detective! Peter tiptoed back to the door and listened.

He heard nothing. The door was a heavy, old-fashioned door which excluded conversation. Peter passed on to the front door, and, opening it, looked out. The chauffeur, who was reading a time-worn sporting newspaper, glanced up and then continued reading. Peter eyed the luggage piled upon the back seat of the car, and advanced casually.

'Are you Alfred?' demanded Hackett with nasal severity.

Alfred started up with a guilty look and brought his tankard into immediate and prominent notice by hiding it beneath the cottage chair.

'Ay, ay,' he said.

The strange gentleman tapped his stick on the floor before him, leant forward upon it with both hands, and assumed an attitude of withering mastery over Alfred.

'The landlady is out, I understand? Are you the only representative of the hotel who is at home?'

Alfred directed a watery gaze past the stranger towards the door. He slowly gained his feet and stood scratching his neck.

'I don't know,' he replied.

'This is the only inn in the place, is it not?'

'I don't know,' said Alfred.

'How many guests were there stopping in the hotel last night?'

'I don't know,' said Alfred.

'How many rooms are there for the accommodation of guests?'

'I don't know,' said Alfred.

'Your knowledge,' remarked Claude Hackett, 'appears to be limited. Perhaps you could tell me how many shillings make five.'

'I don't – oh, I might,' said Alfred.

The long, white fingers of Mr Hackett sought his waist-coat pocket.

'Who is the gentleman out there? What is his name?'

'I don't know,' said Alfred.

The fingers were withdrawn from the pocket.

'I don't, honest,' said Alfred.

'Was he staying here last night?'

'I don't – 'e might 'a bin,' said Alfred.

'But it wasn't *he* who—' Hackett broke off with startled eyes. An inspiration of the most objectionable kind appeared suddenly to have possessed him. He advanced towards Alfred a step and gesticulated vigorously with his stick in the direction of the door.

'Was it he who had a lady with him?'

Alfred hesitated, scratched his neck again, blew out his cheeks and avoided Mr Hackett's face.

'Why don't ye ask him hisself?' he finally compromised by suggesting.

'Where is this lady now?'

'I don't know.'

'Is she in the hotel?'

'I don't – no, sir.'

'She is not? Where has she gone?'

'I don't know,' said Alfred.

'What was this lady like in appearance?'

'Oo, she were a good, big woman,' said Alfred fast-idiously.

'A – lady of ample proportions?'

'Ay, she were a good, big woman,' repeated Alfred. 'A good bust on 'er, she 'ad.'

'Indeed,' commented Mr Hackett without enthusiasm. 'A lady of what age?'

'Oo, a young 'un, as women go,' said Alfred.

'She was a lady, was she not?'

'Oo, yes; a lady she were, such as ladies is,' agreed Alfred.

'Then say so. Stay. Had this lady a little dog with her?'

'To be s—' Alfred restrained himself and cocked a thoughtful eye upon the fingers which still lingered in the region of the waistcoat pocket. 'I ain't sure,' he stated.

The fingers left the waistcoat pocket and ascended to their owner's chin. The chin looked longer and thinner than ever, as though the teeth above it were set. But there was more anxiety than anger in Hackett's eyes.

Alfred watched the movement of the fingers critically.

'I ain't at *all* sure,' he said.

Hackett did not ask any more questions. He stood in deep thought for the space of a minute. Then with an effort, as though hardening his heart against his will, he roused himself. He handed Alfred five shillings without a word, and walked to the door.

He returned to the bar almost immediately.

'That room down there seems to be an office.'

'Ay, sir, that it is.'

'Bring me the key of it,' said Hackett.

With a groan which might have represented laziness or embarrassment Alfred retired to the secret lair of the keys in Mrs Spoker's absence, and after considerable fumbling selected the desired specimen. By the time he gained the hall Peter, also, had reappeared upon the scene. The latter walked up to Hackett, who was waiting darkly by the office door, and addressed him with a slightly extravagant air of jauntiness.

'I say, look here, you know, I wish you would let me help you if there's anything I can possibly do for you.'

'Thank you,' replied Hackett with a foreshortened bow of acknowledgment. 'If you will have the kindness to wait for me inside that little room, I think I shall be able to take advantage of your offer.'

'Oh – er – all right,' said Peter, losing a trifle of his bravado. 'But I really meant inside the office here. I mean, I know my way about and all that sort of thing, if you – if I – you know.'

Hackett made no further reply. His eyes rested critically on Peter for a moment. Then he took the key from Alfred's shaky hand and inserted it in the lock.

Peter remained in the passage, rubbing the calf of his left leg gingerly with his right toe. The dilemma in which he found himself was now so awful that he felt he would have welcomed the appearance of Mrs Bone in the front porch almost with relief. For during the few minutes which he had spent in small-talk with the chauffeur outside, Peter, unlike the Glastonbury porter, had taken advantage of Claude Hackett's labels.

> Mr Claude Hackett, M.P.
> Rushcombe Fitz-Chartres.
> Via Bristol and Glastonbury.

For the first fraction of a second the label had conveyed to Peter's mind a distant and not unpleasant impression of past amusement. The truth dawned upon him with a cold shiver which seemed to creep lingeringly down his back. He emitted a little gasp and turned open-mouthed to the inn. He wavered, uncertain whether to hasten, whether to linger, whether to hide.

'Private inquiries!' he repeated below his breath. 'Yes. This is nice. Claude Hackett. Followed hotly by Bones. And I actually hurried here and hurt myself behind with my bicycle saddle.'

Gathering his wits, Peter realised that this Claude Hackett could, after all, have no idea that it had been he who had been the participant in last night's fiasco. His real name had never been mentioned. At the worst Hackett would only have ascertained from some obscure and diabolical agent of rumour that Mrs Hackett had been traced to this retreat in company with a stranger unknown. The thought restored a little of Peter's shattered confidence. Indeed, by cultivating an air of indifferent readiness to assist the investigator, he might be enabled to divert any inexpedient suspicion. It was in this spirit that he accosted Claude Hackett outside the office. The latter's request and the manner in which it was made dampened the spirit not a little.

He knew all. Peter saw that at a glance. But how did he know?

There was something masterful, inexorable in the psychology of Claude Hackett which had a very disturbing effect on Peter; something which made him feel like a little, guilty boy in the presence of a master bent upon ruthless discovery. In fact Peter had an uncomfortable sensation that he was years and years younger and several feet shorter than his antagonist. As he shuffled restlessly in the passage he stole a glance through the glass of the warped shutter. Hackett had the visitors' book open and was examining the entries methodically.

Even then, when he saw his worst suspicions confirmed in the handwriting most familiar to him, Claude Hackett's face revealed to Peter no trace of what was passing in his mind. It remained a long, grim, expressionless mask. He closed the massive book with a snap, and turned away.

Peter retired towards the appointed parlour and lingered in the doorway. Alfred was the first to emerge from the office. To the old man the whole course of proceedings was as baffling as the ritual of a Chinese funeral. Peter eyed him with a sudden suspicion. Perhaps, after all his precautions, this unjust steward had let him down. There certainly was a hang-dog air about Alfred as he returned the glance. Peter summoned him closer with a jerk of the head.

'You haven't told him I was here last night with the lady, have you?'

'No,' replied Alfred in an imitative whisper. 'No, I ain't told 'im. Leastways; no – 'e asked me, ye see.'

'When he asked – did you tell him or did you not?' said Peter with growing misgiving and irritation.

'No, I didn't tell 'im,' croaked Alfred in his somewhat unsuccessful undertone. 'Leastways, 'e asks, yer see, and—'

Both glanced nervously towards the shadows of the office. The tall, portentous figure was emerging. Peter dismissed Alfred with a quick gesture and receded into the parlour.

'You blithering old idiot!' he articulated. 'Give me back my five bob.'

# PART THREE
## 'Go He Must'

# CHAPTER XX

## The Quick Way with Mr Mock

Margaret descended the stairs quickly. In the hall were Lady
Bunter, Sir Stirling Bunter, Mr Mock, Mr Goodie and
Francis, together with a vast and conglomerate disorder of
mackintoshes, wetness and steam.

'Where is Mrs Hackett, Francis?' Lady Bunter was saying.
'Sam dear, I should really leave that mackintosh in the
porch. Oh, here is a telegraph. Now mind you men have
baths.'

'I'm dashed if I have a bath for anybody,' said Mr Mock.

'Not you. The wet ones.'

'I'm not wet,' said Sir Stirling. 'If anyone ought to have a
bath it's you, Fanny.'

'Well, I insist upon Mr Goodie having one,' said Lady
Bunter.

'I'm quate agree'ble,' said Mr Goodie.

'Ah, here is Margaret! My dear, my dear! give me a kiss.
My dear, what a joy to see you! You go and get in, Mr
Goodie.'

The fond old lady drew Margaret into her arms, forgetful
that her mackintosh had been only partially removed, and em-
braced her with great affection and at considerable length.

'This *is* a pleasure,' she continued. 'We were so surprised
and delighted when Mr Mock told us you had arrived. I
thought I had muddled.'

'Told her she hadn't,' said Sir Stirling advancing. 'She
never does. How are you, Margaret?'

'I think I must have nearly muddled,' said his wife, re-
leasing Margaret, 'because the Wykehams haven't come.
Margaret, you know Mr Mock, of course. This is Mr Goodie
– Mrs Hackett. Now do go and pop in, Mr Goodie.'

'Well, there's a telegram,' cried Sir Stirling. 'I expect that's from the Wykehams.'

'Yes, I'll see to it in one minute. My dear Margaret. I am so sorry about your husband having to rush off in that disappointing manner. Mr Mock told us of all your adventures. How funny about the little dog. Kind of the clergyman. Will your husband be able to come back soon?'

'Oh, yes,' said Margaret. 'Almost directly. He had to dash off on some business or other. Some Parliamentary business very likely. I expect he will be here again tomorrow.'

'Oh. But how restless and expensive. How dreadfully one seems to have to dash in order to keep pace with these times. Sam, dear, I do think you might change even if you won't bath.'

'I'm going to change. I should like to have a bath too. But I am not going to have a bath unless you do. You're the person who really wants a bath.'

'Well, we'll see. I may. Let's all go to the library just while you finish your pipe. Not you, Mr Goodie.'

'I haven't finished my pape,' said Mr Goodie.

'Then finish it in your bath. I've never seen such obduracy. You know, Margaret, if we women didn't look after men, they would all die of pneumonia in a week.'

'Yes, I know,' said Margaret softly.

Lady Bunter led the way trippingly to the library. The sun was shining again through the windows, lending additional brightness to the already cheerful comfort of oak and leather. The walls were peopled with the happy old-fashioned creations of Dendy Sadler. From ample shelves smiled the warm bindings of complete editions of Punch, Scott, Dickens, Thackeray, George Eliot and the Hackney Stud Book.

Mr Mock edged, crabwise, to one corner of the room, where on a small table stood the components of another much-needed *stingah*.

'But Margaret.'

Lady Bunter, standing with her short straight back to the

fireplace was studying her telegram with a very puzzled expression.

'This telegraph's from your husband, dear. In London.'

'Oh,' said Margaret coolly. 'He's been very quick.'

'It was sent from London this morning.'

'Well, he can't have sent it then, can he?' said Margaret.

'It's signed Claude Hackett. It says "Please expect me today arriving four thirty Claude Hackett."'

'Perhaps he sent it yesterday,' suggested Margaret, rising casually.

She walked to Lady Bunter's side and stood overlooking her hostess with one arm on the latter's shoulder. Sir Stirling was watching her with critical appreciation. 'Marriage suits Margaret. Fine looking woman,' he thought.

'Well perhaps he did send it yesterday, and I'm muddling,' said Lady Bunter hopefully. 'It says the date of the telegraph here – the 19th. Yes, that was yesterday, wasn't it?'

'Yes,' said Sir Stirling.

'*Mana boleh?*' interrupted Mr Mock. 'Today's the 19th.'

'Oh yes, so it is,' said Lady Bunter. 'Annie Hopwood's birthday.'

'Well, perhaps it was her birthday yesterday,' said Sir Stirling.

'No, darling, the 19th is her birthday.'

'I know it is; but yesterday may have been the 19th.'

'No, it wasn't really. I thought it was for the moment, but I was muddling up. Well, Margaret dear, this telegraph must have been sent today. Oh, my dear, how you squeezed my arm.'

'I'm so sorry,' said Margaret. 'It was only a little squeeze of affection.'

'You darling,' responded Lady Bunter with a ready smile, 'it is lovely to have you back here with us. But this telegraph. I can't account for it. Your husband was with you this morning down here and yet here is a telegraph which he sent off from London at – at eleven. Surely it is very strange and queer and complicated and altogether funny.'

'Well, he couldn't have sent it off himself and that I'll swear,' said Mr Mock, advancing, *stingah* in hand. 'I saw the man myself, didn't I, Mrs Hackett?'

'I didn't know,' said Margaret calmly.

'Well, I saw you drive up in the car. He was in the car, wasn't he?'

'Perhaps,' suggested Margaret abruptly to her hostess, 'he told one of the servants to send it off this morning.'

'My dear,' said Lady Bunter with interest, 'have you servants? How lucky and clever. I am told that in London they are as rare as castles in Spain. I have a friend, Gertrude Box. You know the Boxes, people who had the Gubbins' place for the shooting one year – when was it? She—'

'But, look here, Mrs Hackett.' Mr Mock had stepped to the ladies' side, his yellow face wearing the satisfied grin of the amateur logician. 'How can your husband have told the servant to send the cable saying he was going to arrive today, when, if it hadn't been for your breakdown on the road, you would have been here yesterday?'

'I'm afraid that's too involved for me,' replied Margaret with a rather inaffable smile.

'I'm sure it is for me,' said Lady Bunter. 'It sounds like a riddle of the sphinx. Or do I mean the riddle of the sands?'

Mr Mock directed a shaking finger towards the telegram.

'Now, look here,' he said. 'You and your husband started off yesterday in a car intending to get here. But you had a smash or something and had to put up at a rest-house. Your servants didn't know that. They can't have sent the cable. If your husband was with you down here, *he* can't have sent it. Besides, he says he's going to arrive by the train getting here at 4.30. He's not. He's been here once. It's one of the queerest things I've ever come across.'

'Well, never mind,' said Lady Bunter. 'It will all be explained sooner or later. Who's going to have the bath next?'

Mr Mock turned aside with ill-concealed asperity.

'I'm cursed if I have a bath,' he said. 'I've said so twice.'

'Sam, dear, have you finished your pipe?'

'Yes, all right, all right. Look here, Fanny dear, don't go standing about in those wet things all the afternoon.'

'No, my dear, I am just going up now. Margaret, I suppose we are to take it that your husband is not arriving at 4.30? It's all so complicated that it looks as if we are almost bound to make a muddle.'

'How can the man be going to arrive at 4.30 when he left here for London only two hours back in a motor?' interposed Mr Mock, pointedly.

'I hardly know,' said Margaret, eyeing the obstructionist with some disfavour. 'Does it matter much either way?'

'Not the slightest, except that we shall like to see him as soon as he can possibly come,' said Lady Bunter. 'Come upstairs with me, Margaret. I am going to change. Sam, I do trust you will do the same.'

Mr Mock watched the two women pass in company from the room with a scowl of mortification. He turned almost fiercely to Sir Stirling.

'Women! 'Pon my soul! Here's a damned mystery and nobody seems to take the smallest earthly interest in it. No heads!'

Sir Stirling, in the act of following his wife, glanced at Mr Mock on the way, with a look of fatuous toleration.

'Don't you worry, Mock,' he said. 'Leave it to Fanny. You never need worry over anything on earth if you'll only just leave it to Fanny.'

Margaret overheard this advice, as she followed her hostess across the hall to the staircase. She paid special heed to it, as she happened to be worrying considerably over something on earth at the moment. Within two hours Claude would arrive. Unless she could contrive some means of instructing him, he would inevitably give her away. Even then, all would be well, were it not for the evil presence of Mr Mock. The rather suggestive details of her unhappy experience would make the strongest appeal to him. He would carry the story back and chortle over it with other old yellow, half-civilised, toping men at his club. The story would soon be all over London, for such as cared to hear it. It would proceed without delay to the House and to the constituency.

Margaret quickened her step and overtook Lady Bunter as the latter reached her bedroom door. The younger woman had decided. She would leave it to Fanny.

Fanny seated herself on the bed, removed her shoes and stockings, and began to dry her feet with a face-towel. She had launched forth upon an abstruse reminiscence of bathing in company with Margaret's mother when they were girls of twelve, but Margaret cut her short.

'Dear,' she said, 'listen. I want to explain to you about that telegram.'

'The telegraph – gram – from your husband, or rather, not from him but from the servant or somebody, do you mean? My dear Margaret, you really do not know how fortunate you are to have servants in London.'

'It *was* from my husband.'

'Oh, but how and when? Don't explain if it's very difficult to understand.'

'Claude travelled from London today. The man I was with last night was somebody else.'

'Margaret! Who?'

'Peter Wykeham.'

'Margaret!'

The toe-drying movement continued automatically. Lady Bunter sat upright on the bed with her eyes and mouth opened to their fullest capacity.

'I will tell you exactly what happened. Then you must help me.'

'Margaret!' Lady Bunter paused for two or three seconds, then nodded several times with much intensity. 'Go on,' she said. 'Don't keep me on the horns of – whatever the expression is.'

Margaret told her. Lady Bunter was too horrified to interrupt. From time to time she uttered a little painful squeak, as though instead of drying her foot she was lacerating it, as indeed by this time she unconsciously was. Margaret concealed nothing. She sat in a basket chair in the window and coolly revealed every incident of her progress from Paddington to Rushcombe Fitz-Chartres. The conclusion of the recital found Lady Bunter, barefoot still, circumambulating the bedroom at a disquieted trot. She tore the hat from her head and cast it from her to lighten the already excessive pressure upon her brain.

'So now you understand,' said Margaret. She spoke in a definite and final tone which seemed to disarm expostulation. 'What am I to do about it?'

Lady Bunter's eyes and hair were wild. She made nervous intertwining movements with her fingers. The entire responsibility for Margaret's indiscretion seemed already to have been transferred to the shoulders of Fanny.

'Margaret! Margaret! Margaret! Oh, my dear, Margaret! Oh, Margaret dear!'

'There's nothing to worry about if we can keep it dark,' said Margaret. 'We must keep it dark from Mr Mock.'

'Nothing to worry about! But, my dear, there is. What will your husband say?'

'My husband is as calm and reasonable a man as yours is.'

'Oh, well, he's all right, then. But just think what you have done. What do you suppose the other girl, the Wykeham girl, will think? You don't seem to grasp the true awfulness. You actually slept in the same room as this young man. Even if you hadn't and they thought you had it would be bad enough. You seem to be remarkably calm about it I must say. Although I know there was no actual – harm, I can't help feeling it was really just a tiny bit disgraceful. And so appallingly dangerous. I'm astonished at that Wykeham boy. I should have thought he was the last person to have horrid habits. I dare say he did nothing actually wrong, but he might have had more consideration for you; and, oh, dear Margaret, after all that has happened previously, why didn't you have more consideration for yourself?'

'Well, if you'll only help me to hush it up, no one will be any the wiser or any the worse.'

'But, my dear! Suppose the Wykeham girl takes umb— that word. I dare say you know a great deal better than I do that the very fact of your having been seen in the same inn for the night as this boy, not to say bedroom, is enough to get you divorced.'

'No, darling,' said Margaret gently, 'I shouldn't get divorced because there would be nobody trying to divorce me. I should simply be the co-respondent.'

'Simply!' repeated Lady Bunter with a gasp. 'The calm way in which you take this! Anyhow, I may be muddling about which would be the one to be divorced; but I know, from reading the reports of some of these horrid cases, that it only has to be proved that people stayed together at the same hotel for a night, and then *houp la!* that settles it.'

'Why *houp la?*' asked Margaret patiently.

'What I mean to say is the thing's done – like a conjuring trick.'

'Oh, I think you mean "hey presto",' said Margaret.

'*Houp la* is good enough for me. And it may be *houp la* with you, Margaret, unless something is done.'

'Well, put your shoes on for a start. You'll get cold.'

'I am bursting with heat,' said Lady Bunter.

'I must be the first to see Claude when he comes,' continued Margaret, turning to the window with watchful eyes. 'I will meet him at the station and tell him. Then we can invent some reason for his coming back here so soon and—'

'Oh, Margaret! Margaret! You won't lie, dear?'

'Won't I?' said Margaret.

'No, no, no. We must explain the matter more or less truthfully and yet in a way which will camel – what's that word they used to use in the war?'

'Camouflage. And how do you propose to camouflage it?'

'I don't know. Must we try? We're all old friends here.'

'Mr Mock?'

'Oh, Joe Mock is an old friend of mine. I think he will

hold his tongue if I tell him to. It isn't as if he was a woman.'

Margaret shook her head.

'He strikes me as being rather a mischievous old person. I suppose you can't get rid of him for the afternoon somehow.'

'My dear Margaret, I can't very well drive him out of the house, just because you choose to take young men into your bedroom.'

'No, but you can shut him up. He's so very inquisitive.'

Lady Bunter sighed deeply.

'I'll try,' she said. 'But quite apart from Joe Mock we have the Wykehams to deal with.'

Margaret sighed back.

'I know,' she said. 'I have been haunted all day by a feeling that some one will go and let the whole thing out.'

Lady Bunter had ceased her exercise and stood regarding Margaret with an expression which she considered severe.

'When one thinks, my dear child,' she said, 'of all you have had to put up with before now through being indiscreet, I am simply amazed and bewildered at your having run this risk. It shocks even me. If anyone but you had told me that you had done it I should have refused to believe them. This time, at any rate, they have something to go on. It is dreadful.'

'I don't care two straws,' said Margaret quickly, as she turned from the window and smiled into the piteous wrinkled face, 'so long as nothing is done which can harm Claude. Public men are very exposed to all these sorts of calumnies. If they used his wife's reputation in the constituency to try and ruin his career, I should never forgive myself.'

The words brought a look of the greatest tenderness to Lady Bunter's sensitive countenance.

'You do love your husband very dearly, Margaret?' she asked softly.

'I love him above the earth and all that therein is, the heavens and all the powers therein,' said Margaret earnestly.

'Oh, my dear, hush! isn't that a little profane?'

'My love for him isn't profane anyhow,' said Margaret. 'It is a sacred love.'

'M'yes,' said Lady Bunter. 'I feel I ought to be able to say something rather clever now about your observation of the thing you hold so sacred, but I haven't got the brain, so never mind. But now, quickly, what are we going to do and what are we going to say? Goodness knows what may happen next at almost any moment. Unless we put our heads together we are bound to make a muddle.'

'You suggest,' said Margaret, 'and I'll do whatever you think best unless I can see any glaring miscalculations.'

'Very well, my darling,' responded Lady Bunter, pausing to embrace her protégé. 'But I don't see quite how anyone can suggest anything until we know for certain that your husband and the boy's wife are prepared to condone what you have done. Then, of course, worst of all, there is that parson with the silly name. He has already repeated the whole story to Mr Mock. He is probably at this moment at the other end of the county, telling somebody else.'

Here Lady Bunter was absolutely correct.

'But never mind,' she went on. 'I'll tell Sam of course and see what he suggests. With your help and his I may be able to pull the thing out of the fire somehow.'

Fanny was at grips with trouble again and her spirits rose.

She entered upon the first of her duties immediately. She told Sam. It proved to be a slow task. Sam seemed incapable of understanding Margaret's story; and, when at length he understood it, he refused to believe it. When reassured by Fanny that the story was true, he wasted a good deal of time in blaming young Wykeham. Fanny said she did not think, on the whole, that young Wykeham was more culpable in the matter than Margaret. Sam, upon this, readily agreed with Fanny that Margaret was chiefly to blame. Fanny, on the other hand, inclined to Sam's opinion and exonerated Margaret at the expense of Peter. At the conclusion of half an hour, the interview had resulted in an absolute deadlock: each side refused to yield an inch from support of the view originally expressed by the other.

The discussion then took more practical lines. Fanny's next duty arose, that of devising some means of curbing the curiosity of Mr Mock. In this, too, she consulted Sam. Sam's opinion was that the only practical way of curbing the curiosity of Joe Mock was to clear Joe Mock out of the house and keep him out until all this tyranny were overpassed. From which observation developed suddenly a brilliant inspiration.

It was Fanny's idea. That was agreed upon. As a matter of fact Sam first hit on it, but he attributed it to Fanny; and, since the perpetration of a minor untruth was involved, Fanny preferred that it should not be laid at Sam's door. Wisely she refrained from saying so. Otherwise Sam would have claimed sole author's rights and there would have been another deadlock.

Sam, preening himself in his false feathers, descended the stairs to the library door, paused for a brief facial rehearsal on the mat, and entered. Mr Mock was seated on a settee grumbling indeterminately. Mr Goodie was standing at the fireplace drying his ears.

'My dear fellows,' said Sir Stirling, 'something rather unfortunate has happened.'

'Oh. *Apa matcham?*' growled Mr Mock.

'Just at a most inconvenient time, when you, my dear Joe, are practically an invalid and—'

'What has occurrerred?' asked Mr Goodie.

'It's all my fault. Entirely mine. I don't know how to apologise sufficiently—'

'Oh, what the devil is wrong?' cried Mr Mock.

'Why, this. I've just made a most disagreeable discovery.'

'What is it?' asked Mr Goodie. 'There has note been an accident I hoope?'

'No, but – what d'ye think I've just discovered?'

Only Mr Mock answered the question and his voice was

muffled. It was in his direction that Sir Stirling turned in making his dire revelation.

'I have run completely out of whisky,' he said.

Mr Mock gripped the arm of his settee. He half-rose. His weak eyes were wide and horrified.

'Impossible!' he gasped.

'That,' said Sir Stirling, indicating the dregs of the decanter on the table, 'is all there is left.'

'*Hoi – ya!*' said Mr Mock, following the direction of his host's finger. 'Barely enough for one *stingah*. Not enough. Barely enough for a *sookoo*. But what the devil are we going to do about it? You might have broken it gently, Sam. Thought you said it wasn't anything bad.'

'Of course,' said Sir Stirling, 'if I had only the means of sending to the people who supply me at Taunton, I could get some more straight away.'

'Well, send in Heaven's name!' said Mr Mock.

'I can't go myself. I've something else on. Francis, who generally does it, has another job on hand this afternoon too. All the other servants are busy; besides, I shouldn't let them drive the trap. The car has got to take Fanny out and Wemblow, the chauffeur, is the only man who can drive the trap as well.'

'But almighty Providence! I can drive a trap, can't I? How far is Taunton?'

'Oh, my dear Joe, you're not fit. It's very kind of you, but—'

'Not fit! Good Lord, I've driven a buggy through ten miles of semi-jungle before now with a temperature of 104 with denghi fever. Something must be done. The house can't go dry like this.'

'I shouldn't like you to go alone,' said Sir Stirling, shaking his head sagely. 'Perhaps if Goodie would be so awfully good as to keep you company—'

'I'm quate – I'm agree'ble,' said Mr Goodie, without enthusiasm.

'That will be immensely good of you,' said Sir Stirling.

'The old mare is rather sensitive and she knows you, Goodie. But if you'll go, Joe, in the capacity of buyer, and select a good brand—'

'Right!' said Mr Mock. 'Though it's none of it drinkable these days. All I can do to get some of the stuff down.'

'You're sure you're all right to go, Joe? It won't make your gout worse?'

'Gout? Good night! I haven't got gout. Had a touch of liver, but I've shaken that off. When will the buggy be round?'

'I'll order it. It really is most obliging of you both. I think you had better wait and have tea in Taunton.'

Mr Mock's eyes were shining. He rubbed his bony knuckles.

'Give me a chit to these people,' he said, 'I shan't want tea.'

# CHAPTER XXI

## Seconds in the Ring

That feeling of defenceless juvenility returned to Peter with redoubled force as Claude Hackett followed him, with slow strides, into the parlour of the *Stag*. The very manner in which the door was closed was vividly reminiscent of bygone interviews in which one party had been considerably more pained than the other.

Claude Hackett remained composed and deliberate. He found time to remove a small accumulation of dust from his trousers with his handkerchief. When at last he looked into the shifty eyes of Peter it was with interest, almost, it seemed, with respect.

'Would you oblige me by telling me your name?'

Peter fidgeted and made a rather lame effort to summon fortitude.

'Why?' he returned.

'I have reason to believe that you are a friend of my wife's. I am sure that is sufficient excuse for my curiosity.'

Peter thrust his hands into his pockets and attempted to bore a hole in the carpet with the toe of his boot.

'My name's Wykeham as a matter of fact,' he said.

'Oh? Mr Peter Wykeham?'

'M'm.'

'Oh, yes. You have known my wife for a long time?'

'Oh, rather.'

To Peter's great surprise Mr Hackett stepped forward and extended his hand.

'How do you do?' he said.

'Oh – er – how are you?' responded Peter with growing embarrassment as he limply held the white and supple fingers.

'There is apparently no need for me to tell you who I am,' proceeded Hackett returning to his former position.

'No,' replied Peter glancing at the calm eyes with some enmity. 'I saw your name on your luggage.'

Mr Hackett permitted himself that scarcely perceptible tilt of the eyebrows which his friends had learnt to associate with irony.

'It is my luggage then?'

'Isn't it?' said Peter quickly.

'It seems almost reasonable to harbour a misgiving that *you* might claim it,' said Hackett.

Peter's only reply was a little sniff not far removed from open hostility.

'I must confess,' went on the master of the situation, 'that I am at a loss to understand all that has taken place during the last twenty-four hours. I look to you for a great deal of enlightenment. It appears that my wife failed to reach her destination last night and took refuge here. You were with her.'

'Well, why not?' said Peter.

'You were not with her?'

'Yes, I was.'

'You were. Why?'

'Why not?'

The eybrows were tilted again.

'We seem to be in danger of becoming involved in a vicious circle of conversation,' said Hackett. 'I only desire to learn the circumstances which threw you into company with my wife.'

'Well, if you want to know, we both missed the same train at Paddington.'

'Thank you. And then?'

Peter changed feet and continued his boring operations.

'We both missed the train. My wife caught it.'

'*Your* wife?'

'Yes, my wife. I have a wife.'

'Indeed.'

'Yes indeed,' said Peter chafing beneath the cool sardonic manner of his catechist. 'A very good one too. I suppose I can have a wife if I like?'

'Of your own, certainly,' conceded Hackett. 'But please continue. Your own wife caught the train. My wife missed the train. You missed the train.'

'That's right,' said Peter. 'We were all bound for the same spot, the Bunters'. I, having missed the train, gave your wife a lift down in a car. The car went phut two miles from here. So we came here and stayed here. What more do you want?'

'Only a few details of additional information,' said Hackett, examining the grain of his stick and polishing a portion of it with a wash-leather glove.

Peter fidgeted again. This man galled him more than all the Bones in Christendom. How the devil Margaret could ever have—

'Being a married man with a wife of your own – a very good one—' pursued the even, nasal voice, 'you will sympathise with my desire to ascertain that my wife suffered no evil consequences from this unforeseen mishap. The accommodation here, for instance, seems decidedly limited. She procured some food and a bedroom?'

'Oh, we looked after ourselves all right,' muttered Peter.

'I'm very glad to hear it,' said Hackett. 'So you both procured some food and – bedrooms?'

'Oh, yes,' replied Peter stretching his shoulders in a nonchalant manner and turning towards the window.

'In that case,' proceeded Hackett without the least variation in his dispassionate method, 'I am afraid that you yourself cannot have enjoyed a very tranquil night's rest in the company of the old lady above the bar.'

Peter wheeled round. He could restrain the words which burst from his lips no more easily than he could govern the strange tingling of his skin.

'Stop that, Hackett,' he cried. 'This is a true bill. If you think your wife is capable of doing anything that isn't abso-

lutely decent and honourable, then all I can say is you're
damn well unworthy of her.'

The kind eyes, now close to his, brightened immediately
in a keen appreciation. For once Claude Hackett became
animated to the borders of excitement. He clapped his hand
upon Peter's shoulder and gripped him.

'Don't waste your breath,' he said.

'There was nothing wrong, nothing,' said Peter.

'Wrong!' cried Hackett. 'Who dares suggest that there was
anything wrong? Do you imagine that for a single moment I
ever allowed the thought to cross my mind. Thank you, Mr
Wykeham, you needn't trouble to defend my wife's honour
to me.'

Peter fell back with his mouth open.

'Well, what the dickens is all this buzz about?' he asked in
plaintive amazement.

'Come,' said Hackett, 'we're on level ground now, I think.
Let us be honest with each other.'

'I *am* honest,' said Peter. 'Damn it, I only looked after
your wife and tried to fix her up comfortably. We got into a
bit of a hole, I agree. And when you come along snuffling
about and making sarcastic investigations, naturally I don't
stand up with my hands behind me and work off the whole
unlikely yarn at you like a Sunday School child. I shouldn't
have been doing my duty to Margaret if I had.'

Hackett bowed his head. The ghostly smile flickered over
his countenance and was gone.

'You are right,' he said. 'My discoveries here led me to the
belief that you had become rather entangled between you in
your efforts to secure a night's lodging. Perhaps I allowed
myself to be a little sarcastic at your expense. I will be quite
frank with you. And you, please, will be quite frank with me.
What happened?'

Peter breathed heavily, scratched his nose and sat down
on a horse-hair sofa.

'I don't suppose you'll believe me when I tell you,' he
began.

'In which case,' remarked Hackett, relapsing into his former manner, 'I shall be obliged to possess myself in patience until I hear the true facts from my wife.'

'Well,' said Peter with an effort at concentration, 'what happened was this.'

He paused and scratched his nose again.

'It sounds an awfully thin story,' he groaned.

Hackett adjusted the knees of his trousers carefully and seated himself astride the arm of a chair.

'So much the easier,' he said. 'It hasn't got to penetrate a very narrow mind.'

Peter cocked an ultra-cautious eye upon him.

'Before I begin; I only want to – Look here, you meant – you were absolutely in earnest about what you said about Margaret, when I said about her, how she was absolutely – above suspicion? Because—'

He did not complete the sentence. Hackett held up a protesting hand.

'Come, come,' he said, 'we shall probably find that there is plenty for us to disagree about. I shall very likely say that your precautions for Margaret's comfort last night were extremely ill-considered. Don't let us waste time in harping upon the one subject on which there cannot be the smallest dispute. If you doubt whether I am being honest with you on that subject I shall be in danger of losing my temper. I shook hands with you. I am not Judas, I hope.'

'Well, when you hear this yarn, don't be Pilate. If you're influenced by what ordinary convention thinks an enormity you'll probably get pretty warped over this show.'

'Oh, please come to the point,' said Hackett briefly.

Peter found it far from easy to come to the point. The task had, however, been rendered less complicated by the astonishing revelation that Claude Hackett was an ally. As he proceeded along the treacherous path of his story he stumbled more than once. His companion made no effort either to assist or to implicate him, but sat watching the fireplace steadily, as though his thoughts were far away. Peter gradually warmed to his subject. From the outset he made no attempt at further concealment. On the contrary he reviewed every incident of the previous night with an attention to detail which threatened at times to become laborious. Whether Claude Hackett found it laborious or not was impossible to determine. As the narrative approached its most poignant point Peter glanced more than once with supplicatory eyes at his auditor. But the latter made no sign.

The car journey, the leak in the radiator, the long footslog to the *Stag*, the reception accorded them by Mrs Spoker, the complete occupation of Mrs Spoker, the incident of the undesirable friend of 'Arry 'Ook, the departure of the Loves, the furtive plans for utilising the parlour as a sleeping apartment, the arrival of the inevitable and undesirable Sloley-Jones, the banishment of Pansy, the wangling of the visitors' book, every episode was recorded with explicit, if occasionally rather grandiose veracity. Then came the test.

Peter faltered, pulled himself together with a little shake of the chin and plunged boldly on. The impassive figure opposite never stirred a hair.

The locked doors, the ensuing arguments (complete with reiteration of the comparative indelicacy of riding upon buses and sleeping upon floors); the bed on the floor, the window, the voice of Pansy *in extremis*, the descent and wetting, the return. The broken basin. The visitation of Mrs Spoker. The bed. A nervous glance here. Peter gulped and hastened on.

The rest was easier going. Peter deposited Margaret at the Bunters', heard of the fatal activities of Sloley-Jones, returned with Dann, left Dann on the high road and telephoned from Downblotton; received warning of the Bones, bicycled back to the *Stag* upon a rack and—

'Well, there you are,' said Peter. 'And I suppose you'll say I've made a howling mess of things.'

Hackett opened his eyes a trifle, but did not raise them from the fireplace.

'Yes,' he answered. 'But only because I cannot hit upon a more expressive word than "howling" at the moment.'

'Well, I'm awfully sorry,' said Peter.

'My wife – Margaret' – Hackett leant back very slowly and looked at Peter – 'is a woman quite without any rival in sympathy and understanding. I am very loath to think that any advantage should have been taken of that sympathy.'

'None was,' said Peter anxiously.

'There I entirely disagree with you,' said Hackett. 'However, if we are going to proceed together to the Bunters', please don't tell Margaret that I think so. I shouldn't like her to think that I did not approve of one of her kind actions.'

'By Jove,' Peter exclaimed almost involuntarily, 'you are an extraordinarily good sort of fellow, Hackett.'

The manner in which his confession had been received had banished his bashful timidity in one instant.

'I am a reasonable man, that's all,' replied Hackett. 'And, being a reasonable man, I expect you to comply with a favour which I have to ask you.'

'Of course I will,' said Peter. 'What is it?'

'You will consent to come with me to the Bunters'. You will forgive me if I consider your story so unique as to require confirmation before I definitely accept it.'

'Yes,' said Peter with a slightly mournful laugh. 'I suppose that's reasonable enough. All right. I'll come along with you if you want me.'

'You see, Wykeham,' said Hackett more pointedly, 'if, when I have heard the really official version, I find that it does not tally with yours; if, that is to say, I discover that some definite advantage has been taken of my wife, I shall appreciate having the man who took that advantage close at hand.'

'I shan't run away,' said Peter. 'You'll find the facts are exactly as I've told you.'

'Thank you,' said Hackett politely. 'Then that is agreed.'

'Of course,' said Peter, 'I shall have to wait until I've seen my wife and her crowd. I hope I shall be able to bring her along too, if you can tackle both of us. She may cut up rough and refuse to come. I expect she's been pretty well primed by her mother.'

Hackett's gaze returned to the fireplace. He tilted his eyebrows as he deliberated.

'Does your wife's mother know the facts of the case?' he asked.

'No, but she'll jolly soon find 'em out,' said Peter pessimistically.

'Don't you think it might be advisable to keep your wife partially in ignorance of all that occurred until you have the opportunity of explaining to her alone?'

'Yes, but it can't be done,' replied Peter.

'Why? I may tell you I should never have come to this place, had I not, by a strange coincidence, chanced upon an informant whom I now have no difficulty in identifying as your friend, Sloley-Jones.'

'That scheming, meddling mendicant!' cried Peter.

'It is hardly likely that he will waylay your wife's family as well,' said Hackett suggestively. 'They must be relying entirely upon conjecture as to your – behaviour. If we can mollify their suspicions, surely that will have the desired effect?'

'Oh, well,' said Peter, 'personally, of course I'm prepared to lie like a trooper if only I can put Mrs Bone off the scent. She wouldn't take it like you have. But, naturally, I'm not asking you to chime in and lie too.'

Hackett rose quite suddenly. The quick movement was unusual in him. It was as though he had recalled to mind an appointment which he had failed to keep. His expression, too, was changed. The kindness had left his eyes.

'Look here, Wykeham,' he cried. In his voice rang a new note of stern challenge. 'I was driven to this inn by a haunting fear; a fear that the thing I hold more precious because it has been foully wounded once was in danger. I mean my wife's reputation. I've little enough to thank you for. You've taken very pretty measures to guard her name from some of her dear friends. Be that as it may, the danger's present, and by any means in my power, fair or foul, I'm going to squelch it.'

'Good man!' cried Peter rapturously. 'I'm damned sorry for what I've done and you can trust me to back you up in the squelching for all I'm worth.'

'Very well,' said Hackett more collectedly. 'Your best plan will be to persuade your wife to accompany us to the Bunters'. Who else is to be expected?'

'Her mother and father. The father's all right. He won't give any trouble. He's a poop. The mother is like one of those females of the classics with snakes instead of hair.'

'I think, perhaps, you had better allow me to deal with the mother,' suggested Hackett.

'My dear fellow, do,' consented Peter in the most generous tone.

'What time do you expect these people?'

'Judging from what I heard on the telephone I thought they'd be here now. What about fortifying ourselves? You help to make the laws; help me to break one for a change.'

Claude Hackett, now completely restored to his former almost lethargic ease, consulted his watch and nodded.

'Yes,' he said. 'I think I may as well have a whisky and soda.'

'I think you're wise,' said Peter presciently.

# CHAPTER XXII

## Thin Ice

'This is the place,' shouted Mrs Bone, rapping the window of the car with the butt end of an umbrella. 'Stop! Will you stop! Driver! Tell him to stop; this is the place. Stop, driver! Ferdinand, will you wake up and tell him! Stop, I say. This, thank goodness, is the miserable place.'

Mr Bone aroused himself with a jerk which dislocated his grey bowler.

'Sorry, my dear,' he said. 'I was asleep. Dropped off. Where are we?'

'Blotto,' replied Mrs Bone with asperity. 'Get out.'

Mr Bone turned incredulously to the driver.

'Is this Blotto?' he asked.

The driver, who seemed far from certain on this point, was craning his neck to look backwards towards the inn they had just passed.

'Looks like it,' he admitted.

'Oh. Well, it's been a long way,' said Mr Bone.

'Yessir. A good bit longer than I estimated.'

'I suppose you've come by the shortest route?'

'Of course I have,' said the driver. 'Why shouldn't I have?'

'We seem to have been half over Somerset,' said Mr Bone meekly.

'So we have bin,' said the driver. 'This *is* 'alf over Somerset.'

'Oh,' said Mr Bone.

'Will you get out?' said Mrs Bone.

'Half a moment, Constance. The man is going to back I think. You will back the car to the inn, please. All right, my dear; one moment. I knew a man who broke his leg getting out of a car when it was being backed.'

'I'm not surprised,' said Mrs Bone. 'Just the sort of fool you do know.'

'Look out,' said Mr Bone. 'There's another car there. Don't run into it.'

The driver gave vent to a brief appreciation of this advice beneath his breath and brought his car to rest, after sundry manoeuvres, in the rear of Claude Hackett's. Mrs Bone dismounted and sniffed the air of Blotto menacingly. Sophia followed her. Mr Bone, who had been issuing instructions to the driver, turned a little nervously to his better half.

'What?' exclaimed the latter. 'Says he can't wait here long? Let me speak to him. Get the bag from inside the car. I will speak to the man. Will you try and keep out of the way for one moment of time?'

Mrs Bone thereupon turned her back to the inn and challenged the driver. Mr Bone read the inscriptions on the bar and parlour windows and pretended not to. Sophia, after regarding the whole of the exterior with an expression of puzzled disdain upon her handsome face, moved towards the inn door and tested the handle. Next moment, with a stifled cry, she found herself clasped in the arms of Peter.

Found herself; for, in the first shock of this unexpected greeting, she certainly lost herself. Then, after a momentary struggle, she saw who it was, realised with a sudden rush of emotion that the husband upon whom all her affections had been centred in growing expectation and renewed hope throughout that day's long, weary journey, held her as a lost child clings to the mother restored. The floodgates of Sophia's better nature were loosened.

'Peter! Peter, my darling!' she cried, and fell upon his neck.

He drew her into the parlour, his arms around her still, reluctant to release her. In the hall doorway the face of Mr Bone peered stupidly like that of some surprised beast.

'Sit down here, my dear one,' said Peter. 'How tired you

must be. Don't let's start explanations and things for a minute. You will want a breather after all this.'

'I only want you,' said Sophia. 'Stay here with me.'

'You bet,' said Peter.

Sophia turned her attention to the tall figure standing with his back towards them by the window.

'Who?' she whispered a little apprehensively.

'Oh, Mr Hackett!'

The figure turned.

'Mr Hackett is a friend of ours,' explained Peter. 'He is all part of the – mess up. He is the husband of the lady I was talking to when the train left Paddington. And oh, Sophia, I am frightfully sorry about that effort.'

Sophia seemed to pay small heed to the apology. She was smiling quite amiably and shaking hands with Mr Hackett. After all, if the husband knew all and remained on the best of terms, there could be little for her to worry about.

'Oh, so you are still here?'

Mrs Bone had appeared in the doorway and was taking stock of the situation with a pose which seemed incomplete without a lorgnette. She relinquished this in order to turn her head with a sudden movement of annoyance which suggested that she was being prodded from the rear.

'Yes,' said Peter. 'At least, I came back here when I heard you were coming. How awfully jolly to see you all down here. May I introduce Mrs Bone – Mr Hackett?'

Mrs Bone appeared rather uncertain as to whether he might. She advanced two short paces and bowed coldly.

'And Mr Bone,' proceeded Peter cheerfully. 'Where is he?'

'Come into the room,' commanded Mrs Bone.

'I couldn't before,' expostulated the husband.

'And close the door.'

'All right. Give us a chance,' said Mr Bone.

'S'sh,' said Mrs Bone. 'This is my husband,' she added bluntly to Hackett.

'So I – How do you do?' replied the latter.

Peter was on his feet at Sophia's side. He still held her hand.

'I should like to tell you all for a kick-off – for a start,' he said, 'that Mr Hackett is the husband of the lady I was talking to at Paddington when I missed the train.'

This announcement rather took the wind out of the sails of Mrs Bone, who, ever since setting eyes upon Peter, had been silently contemplating a dramatic opening and had decided upon 'And is your mistress still with you?'

'Yes, I am very sorry that Mrs Wykeham should have been so inconvenienced.'

It was Hackett who spoke, and he made a formal little bow of apology to Sophia as he did so.

'From the purely selfish point of view, the oversight suited my wife and myself admirably,' he continued. 'It enabled Wykeham to offer her a lift in his car. He, of course was anxious to follow Mrs Wykeham without delay. I followed her in *my* car.'

Peter looked up amazed at the coolness and calculation with which this refined liar was taking charge of the situation. Sophia's expression was wistful but satisfied. Mr Bone was murmuring involved sentences of trite gratification. Mrs Bone silenced him with a flourish of the hat and breathed heavily through her nose.

'Oh,' she said. 'But may one ask why your wife didn't wait and come with you?'

'One is naturally prompted to do so,' replied Hackett amiably but with complete gravity. 'I expected to be detained indefinitely by a deputation of constituents, which, however, failed to materialise.'

Mr Bone uttered a little coo of reverential interest.

'Are you an M.P.?' he asked.

'I have that peculiarity,' said Hackett. 'It has ceased, I am afraid, to be "that honour".'

'Oh, I don't know. H'm. By Jove. Fancy!' said Mr Bone, pulling down his waistcoat and smiling very affably.

Mrs Bone was making restless movements of the shoulders and lips. She returned, undefeated yet, to the attack.

'So you heard that this – son-in-law of mine had brought this – wife of – your wife to this – inn; and followed them here?'

Hackett bowed acquiescence.

'Exactly,' he said. 'I happened, fortunately, to hear that they had met with a mishap and had taken refuge here. So I came here too.'

Mrs Bone contented herself with murmuring 'Very fortunately indeed, I should think' beneath her breath, and with directing a glance at Peter which only had the effect of tightening the clasp of Sophia's fingers.

'Seems a funny sort of pub,' remarked Mr Bone, who rather flattered himself that he was rescuing his wife from an embarrassing predicament with considerable conversational skill. 'They seem to leave you to your own devices. Where's the landlord?'

'The landlady's out,' said Peter. 'There's nobody about.'

'Oh? I thought I saw an old man looking out of the window.'

'Oh, he's the barman.'

'The barman, is he? Well, I may as well go and have a word with him,' said Mr Bone carelessly.

'Why?' demanded Mrs Bone in a subdued but threatening tone.

'Oh. Just to – tell him we – don't want anything.'

'Stay here, please. I may as well tell you,' said Mrs Bone with severity to Hackett, 'that we accompanied my daughter here, because we heard that my son-in-law was at this place with—'

She hesitated and pursed up her lips. A china ornament on the mantelpiece apparently distracted her.

'With us?' suggested Hackett gently.

Mrs Bone still made no reply. Every moment seemed to make it increasingly difficult to explain to this cool, unexpected husband exactly why she *had* accompanied her daughter there.

'Didn't you think it was quite nice for me to be here with Mr and Mrs Hackett?' asked Peter, carrying the war into the enemy's camp with some foolhardiness.

Mrs Bone seemed to relish this interruption. She wheeled on Peter. The very hairs of the bearskin coat she wore seemed to bristle.

'All we knew was that you had abaondoned Sophia in the train and that you were last seen in company with another lady. I, for one, was not surprised. When we heard that you had brought the lady to this inn for the night, I, for one, pricked up my ears. Perhaps if Mr – hum – here knew some of your lady friends, he would not be so ready to allow Mrs – hum – his wife to go motoring in your company.'

'Oh!' replied Peter, grasping Sophia's hand tighter than ever. 'Have you any evidence that I have neglected Sophia in any way, since we married?'

'Your reputation before your marriage, I think, justifies a certain amount of precaution in the matter,' returned Mrs Bone, in sweeping and grandiloquent sarcasm.

'Gosh!' was Peter's sole and rather obscure comment to this.

'May I interrupt by suggesting that what has been an evident misconception, however plausible, has been cleared up?' said Hackett. 'I'm anxious to be getting under way for the Bunters'. If Mrs Wykeham is ready to make another motor journey, I shall be very glad to give her and her husband a lift.'

'Oh, but I can't go there tonight,' said Sophia. 'Nor can Peter. We – I, that is, left all our clothes at home.'

'It's no good going all the way up to London and down again just for our clothes,' said Peter. 'It'll be all right if we don't have any clothes at the Bunters' just for the first night. The Bunters are awfully simple sort of people. We can telephone for our clothes from Downblotton or send a wire. They'll be down tomorrow.'

Sophia looked inquiringly up into her husband's face. She knew that the prospect of making the return journey to London in company with her parents and the reclaimed Peter was even more odious than that of casting herself upon the mercy of Lady Bunter with a teagown and a toothbrush. Then again came the vision of a smart country house party; of herself, shorn of all her saving appurtenances, being subjected to the critical gaze of the guests. As she hesitated an inspired solution occurred to her.

'What did you sleep in last night, Peter?' she asked.

'Oh, a bed,' replied Peter in an off-hand manner.

'Yes, but what did you wear?'

'Wear? Oh, I borrowed some – some wear.'

'Oh. How did you manage that?'

'Well, as a matter of fact, I managed to borrow some stuff from the hotel. It was pretty rough, but it served.'

'I told you,' said Hackett kindly, 'that before you decided to spend the night as you did you should have consulted me.' He turned to Sophia with his fleeting smile. 'I could have supplied him with more suitable arrangements,' he added.

Sophia smiled back.

'Because I was thinking,' she went on to Peter, 'that we might stay here tonight. Mother could have our things sent down tomorrow.'

Mrs Bone, who had been reinforcing herself by opening the door and making a further brief reconnaissance of the dingy hall and staircase, returned in time to notice the grimace of sharp apprehension on Peter's face and wondered what she had missed.

'It surprises me,' she said, addressing Hackett, 'that you should all have found room to sleep in this place.'

'The accommodation is not very extensive,' acknowledged Hackett.

'How many bedrooms are there?' asked Sophia of Peter keenly. She could see no reason why the proposal to spend the coming night at the *Stag* should not solve the whole difficulty.

'Two,' said Peter. He shifted his position uncomfortably and glanced at his mother-in-law, who was watching.

'Oh, there *are* two bedrooms then,' said that lady with a movement of the shoulders which seemed to imply that she was suffering from an irritation between the blades.

'Where are they?' asked Sophia.

Mrs Bone did not fail to detect the little frown of discouragement with which Peter greeted this cross-examination.

'One is over this room.' It was Hackett who spoke. He addressed the remark to the whole company. 'The other is opposite. Above the bar.'

'Oh, is *that* where the bar is?' soliloquised Mr Bone.

'Well, we should only want one, shouldn't we?' said Sophia. 'Which did you have last night, Peter?'

'The one above here; but – it's awfully uncomfortable. I simply couldn't allow you to—'

He dropped his voice to a whisper and, seating himself on the arm of the horse-hair sofa, engaged his wife in earnest confidence. She warmed to his ardent consultations for her comfort. All her bitterness had long since vanished. She was smiling and winsome as any maiden in playful argument with her sweetheart.

Mrs Bone did not intend to be left out of this. She advanced a step or two and listened unblushingly. Suddenly a thought struck her and she turned again to Hackett.

'Did you and Mrs – hum – find the other room very uncomfortable too?' she asked.

'My wife failed to get a wink of sleep in it all night,' he answered with dignified resentment.

'H'm.' Mrs Bone inclined her ear again to the whispered controversy, hovering menacingly like a cat preparing to spring upon the innocent discussions of two mice.

Peter was finding the very reasonable proposal of Sophia exceedingly difficult to contravene. He was becoming more involved, his arguments were growing more specious every moment. Sophia made no secret of her antipathy to the proposed arrival at the Bunters' with her toothbrush and her teagown. Peter, too, had no clothes, dress or undress. Here they were at the *Stag* with a room awaiting them. What could be more reasonable than to avail themselves of the inn for the one more night? As Peter fidgeted and stumbled and glanced nervously towards the window, Mrs Bone sprang.

'Yes,' she said. 'Most practicable and proper. I cannot have Sophia appearing at strange country-houses like a savage. Moreover, your father-in-law will leave you his pyjamas. Ferdinand, do not chew your hat. Open the bag.'

Mr Bone sighed, laid down his hat and commenced operations as dictated. His wife superintended the unpacking of Sophia's belongings and of his own striking Swan-stripe slumber suiting, which the poor man exhibited with the rather shamefaced manner of a schoolboy whose over-fond mother has decked him in ridiculous attire. Sophia leant back on the horse-hair sofa with a little chuckle of satisfaction. Peter seized the opportunity to steal one last, despairing glance of entreaty at Hackett.

The latter did not appear to notice it. He bestirred himself slowly and moved across the room towards the door.

'I must really be preparing to leave,' he said. 'I agreed to go to the Bunters' this afternoon, and my wife, no doubt, thinks that I am already on my way.'

In the doorway he turned and addressed himself pointedly to Peter. In the depths of his genial eyes there was the faintest possible glimmer of innuendo.

'You will decide whether you are coming with me, won't you?'

'Thank you so much. We are going to stay here,' said Sophia.

'Ah,' said Hackett. 'Well, I am going to see my wife.'

The door closed behind him, but his footfall could be heard a moment later on the stairs.

'Where is he off to now? Where is his wife then?'

Sophia had turned quickly to Peter. The latter was gazing upwards towards the corner of the ceiling. His face wore a smile of fatuous solicitude. Sophia noticed it with a shadowy frown of misgiving. Mrs Bone, too, was all attention.

Peter lowered his eyes and banished the fond smile. He saw, with complete satisfaction, that it had taken full effect.

'The idea is,' he explained, 'that the lady up there is not fit to go on today. You see, she had a very trying and tiring experience. However, she won't let Hackett stay with her. We haven't been able to communicate with the Bunters, and I suppose they will be expecting the Hacketts just as they are expecting us. She's expecting to go from here tomorrow. She said something about feeling as if she wanted to go home, but—'

'Oh, so that woman is still here?' cried Mrs Bone.

'Yes, rather. She's still here.'

'But her husband is leaving her here?'

'Yes. I say; she doesn't want Hackett to delay pushing on to the Bunters'.'

'She can't be feeling very ill,' said Sophia darkly.

'Oh, I don't think she's really at all ill,' said Peter. 'Just tired and so on.'

'Is she still in bed?' asked Mrs Bone severely.

'Yes, she's staying in bed today,' answered Peter. 'She's in bed in the room above the bar.'

'But who's looking after her, now that her husband's going?' asked Sophia.

'Oh, I don't think she wants anyone to look after her,' said Peter. 'But now that I am going to stay here – and you, of course—'

'Who is at the Bunters', do you know?' said Sophia, her dark eyes roaming in contemplation.

'No one practically but the Hacketts and ourselves,' said Peter.

'Because I think I'd rather change my mind and go on there with you and Mr Hackett now,' said Sophia.

# CHAPTER XXIII

## 'Lhude Sing Cuccu'

Sophia's decision was obviously final. She arose quickly and gathered the garments which her father had managed with considerable disorganisation to transfer from the bag to the floor of the parlour.

'Tell Mr Hackett, please, that we will go with him after all. And get some paper from somewhere,' she said to Peter.

'Righto,' said Peter.

Disguising as best he could the elation which this development had wrought in him, he passed from the room into the bar. He was conscious that his movements were being followed with no little interest by his father-in-law, whose offer to lend a hand met, however, with a brief but unqualified veto from the parlour.

Pausing only to impress upon Alfred the necessity of remaining absolutely natural and devoid of the smallest semblance of intelligence. Peter secured some sheets of newspaper and returned. Even when confronted with the prospect of making her bow at the Bunters' with her worldly possessions enclosed in the advertisement sheets of a Sunday paper, with the song of the week, 'I went on eating my banana,' conspicuous to every eye, Sophia never wavered in her determination. At the worst she would go to bed on arrival at the Knoll and stay there until her clothes came from London. Anything was better than remaining at this wayside inn, with the rival who had lured Peter from his place of duty awaiting his ministrations in the bedroom above the bar.

Sophia was no longer jealous, no longer resentful. She knew that her influence over Peter was supreme, so long as she could remain at hand to exercise it. But she had seen that foolish, infatuated grin on his face as he gazed upwards towards the room where Mrs Hackett lay. She almost pitied the poor boy in his weakness. She could afford to now. The embrace with which he had greeted her on her arrival had been proof enough of his penitence and true devotion. But he was easily led astray; and Sophia's quick temper had flared up again for one harsh second, as her thoughts turned to that languid seductress in her stronghold above the bar. The husband, good, easy man, was only too obviously a tool in her hands. Why had she persuaded him to go away and leave her? No, no; the atmosphere of this inn was not calculated to prove very beneficial to poor Peter. She would remove him at all costs and by the quickest possible means.

Together at the Bunters' they would stroll in the woods and she would recall all the sweet early raptures of their happy marriage. She knew he would yield to her influence as he had yielded himself to her arms at their moment of meeting just now. And when Mrs Hackett arrived at the Bunters' – Sophia smiled at the thought. She would be ready for her.

So off they went, with Hackett. Little time was wasted. Neither Peter nor Mrs Bone made any overtures towards apology or reconciliation. Sophia merely instructed her mother to have all the clothes she would require dispatched by passenger train without fail on the following morning. Peter found time to bribe the Bones' driver and to suggest that the latter should refuse to remain at the *Stag* for more than, at the most, five minutes longer. This small negotiation was conducted in the highest possible spirit of concord.

Mrs Bone remained in the parlour. She heard the engine of the car, the changing of gears, the warning toot of the horn. She glanced through the window just in time to see a little cloud of dust on the road leading to the church and the small black cottages. She relapsed on to the horse-hair sofa. She was silent and ruminating. She had tasted defeat; and worse, she saw in her husband's solid expression of sagacious boredom the unkindest cut of all.

'Oh, don't grin,' she said suddenly.

'Not,' retorted Mr Bone concisely.

'Well, don't nibble your bowler hat. I've told you already.'

'All right, Constance. It's no good being sick about it. We ought to be very glad.'

'Who's being sick?' said Mrs Bone.

'Of course I knew all along that Wykeham was a perfectly straight and decent young chap. You would have it he was a blackguard. Now I've proved you wrong, let's go home.'

'You have proved me wrong! As if you would have come down here if it hadn't been for me.'

'Well, it was hopeless waste of time, I agree,' said Mr Bone. 'Anyhow, let's go home now.'

'I want some tea,' said his wife.

'Oh, I'll go to the bar and see if I can get you some if you like.'

'You want to go and drink again, I know,' said Mrs Bone.

'Yes, I do. I could do with another drink of beer quite easily.'

'Do you suck beer like this all day long when you are supposed to be at the office?'

'No, but I want a drink now. So do you; you've just said so. One man's drink is another man's – or rather – one man's beer is another—'

'Oh, stop talking rubbish,' said Mrs Bone.

'I don't expect you can get any tea here,' continued Mr Bone, stooping to repack the bag. 'But you can get some tea at Bristol. In the buffy. Or, perhaps, you may be able to buy some on the way and take it in your hand in the car.'

With this Parthian shaft the triumphant husband retired with the bag into the hall.

Mrs Bone chose to ignore it. She leant back upon her couch and closed her eyes, as though in prayer. She opened them again almost at once.

Machine-gun practice in the road.

'You!'

'You!'

The voice of her husband and Cathcart Sloley-Jones

blended in a crescendo of astonished cordiality from the front door.

'I've got Constance inside there,' she heard the former remark at the conclusion of these preliminaries. 'I've got!' Mrs Bone resented that way of making the announcement.

'What are you doing here? Come inside,' she commanded.

'Look 'ere. I can't stay messing around 'ere indefinitely any longer,' cried the voice of the Bristol hireling from the roadway.

'All right, all right. Just coming,' replied Mr Bone.

'That man has been engaged and must do what he is ordered,' said Mrs Bone sharply. 'Come in, Cathcart. Where have you come from?'

'Damned – going on – messing abart – damned – going back,' came in contemptuous snatches of protest from the road.

'How do you do, Constance? The last person I expected to see here, absolutely. Well, I'm jiggered. By Jove. Fancy this now. My hat!' said Sloley-Jones entering the parlour and greeting his cousin.

'S'sh. S'sh. All right. In one moment.' Mr Bone's voice could be overheard to promise in the hall.

'Why are you here, Cathcart?'

'As a matter of fact I ought to have been here long ago. I had some awfully hard luck with my bike. I've been suffering a lot of trouble of one sort or another lately. This time it was my sprockets, I think, chiefly. I think I got some oil on my magneto as well. You know if you get oil on your magneto, you're done. I cleaned my magneto of course; and then I found I was vibrating and popping.'

'Never mind about your bicycle. I wish to know what you are doing, coming to this inn?'

'Not ruddy well your property – engaged to drive – not to ruddy well pose—'

'All right. All right. Constance dear, when do you think?'

'Come inside this room and close the door. It is not very pleasant to have a husband who is afraid of a rude man.'

'But the man wants to know—'

'Come inside and shut the door,' said Mrs Bone.

'Just coming. Je-ust coming,' said Mr Bone to the road-way, as he unwillingly obeyed.

'I say, look here, don't let me keep you, you know – what-ever happens,' said Sloley-Jones. 'I was really coming to this inn to – well, to see somebody else. Tremendous surprise to me this. Weird.'

'Whom were you coming to see?' asked Mrs Bone, leaning forward, dropping her voice and directing a very stealthy glance at her husband.

'Well, as a matter of absolute fact, I was following some-body. The whole business is rather strange. I happened to meet a man at Glastonbury, and to tell him about this inn and some people I knew who were stopping here last night; and he immediately leapt on a car and dashed off here. So I naturally followed. I mean to say. It struck me that perhaps I had told him too much. Shall I tell you all about the whole thing?'

'Yes,' said Mrs Bone with growing intensity. 'Ferdinand, do sit still. Why must you waggle your hands about?'

'The man's come round to the window,' said Mr Bone.

Mrs Bone rose snorting.

'Your whole life seems to be spent in fear and trembling of men,' she said.

She sailed from the room. Within two minutes she was back. The driver had returned, a mere crushed worm to the seat of his car, where he remained formulating hopeless little designs for turning.

'Now,' said Mrs Bone.

In course of time the driver recovered. He stirred slowly in the seat. He was thawing into shame of his outraged import-ance. He had allowed his dignity to be openly disgraced. He had been ticked off by a ratty old woman. Again he scrambled from his seat, jerked his head in the manner which indicates decision in a gentleman of his nature, and again sought the parlour window.

Mrs Bone sat forward on the horse-hair sofa. Her eyes were staring wildly at the opposite wall, as though she saw a vision; but in the quick puckering of her lips there was an insinuation of relish. Her hat was awry. She was making little pinching movements of the thumb and first finger of either hand.

Seated at the little table where Peter and Margaret had partaken of dinner the night before, Mr Bone was, unmolested now, chewing the brim of his grey bowler with fervent relish. There was little change in his usual facial expression of obstinate stupidity.

Sloley-Jones stood at the fireplace. His great, dirty hands were outspread before him in gesticulation. His spectacles looked larger than usual. He was speaking impressively; arguing, it seemed. Whenever he ceased doing so his mouth remained open and he turned to Mrs Bone with a forlorn smile of protesting innocence.

Mrs Bone turned on him suddenly, delivering, to judge from her appearance, some devastating ultimatum. The parson wavered, nervously buttoning and unbuttoning the top button of his Norfolk jacket. Then, with a gesture of unwilling assent, he crossed the room and opening the door climbed rather laboriously up the staircase. Outside the door of the bedroom above the bar he halted and knocked timorously. As the response came from within he screwed his head round, rather in the manner of a blackbird investigating a doubtful worm. Then he entered the bedroom.

He had left the parlour door ajar. Greatly daring, the driver entered the hall and was about to renew his attentions to his clients when he overheard the altercation which was proceeding within and paused to listen.

'So now who's the fool?'

'I don't believe it even now. It's all rot. I'm going home.'

'Are you? I am going to Rushcombe Fitz-Chartres.'

'Nonsense, Constance. You can't do that.'

'I am going to.'

'Well, I'm not. The whole thing can be explained, I expect. We've made one hopeless hash and—'

'You are afraid of coming and saving Sophia from—'

'Yes, all right. I'm afraid. I bet you this fellow, Cathcart, is making some ridiculous mistake. I'm not going to burst into other people's houses and make a damned fool of myself for anybody.'

'Not for Sophia?'

'I tell you there's nothing to show that Soph—'

'Not for me?'

'No,' said Mr Bone courageously. 'I'm going back to Bristol in time to catch the 5.30.'

'You realise what this means? You are leaving me?'

'Oh, nonsense, Constance. I simply—'

'Very well. Go. Thank goodness I have got Cathcart to look after me.'

'All right. Only don't go and lug the poor devil into more trouble. You don't want to get our family a name for—'

'The next time anybody hears your family name,' said Mrs Bone leaning forward at her husband, 'will be in the divorce reports if I don't have my way and you have yours.'

'Oh, Lord,' moaned the wretched Mr Bone. 'What are you going to do now?'

'I am going to tell Sophia that her husband spent last night in the same bed as Mrs Hitchcock. I am going to see her husband and I am going to see Mr Hitchcock. If, as I suspect, that is not really Mrs Hitchcock in that room up there, I am also going to see Mrs Hitchcock. I am going to show all these people that, even if my daughter has married into a gang of vile and dissolute people, she is not going to be made a victim of their loathsome Society practices.'

'How are you going to get there?' asked Mr Bone brightening suddenly.

'I shall take the car on to Rushcombe Fitz-Chartres immediately.'

'You won't,' said the driver dramatically in the doorway.

Mrs Bone drew herself up, quivering.

'Oh, so you are here, listening to our private conversation, are you?'

'I am that,' said the driver.

He turned to Mr Bone.

'Coming back to Bristol with me now?' he inquired. 'Say yes or for ever 'old your tongue.'

Mr Bone wilted.

'You know really, Constance,' he began, fingering the bag.

'Go then. Go,' cried his wife. 'Leave the bag and go.'

'No, but I don't want to go and—'

'You do. You have said so. Go and leave me.'

'Constance, I—'

'I'm just going to start the car up,' whispered the driver warningly.

'Oh, Lord. All right, I jolly well will go,' said Mr Bone.

He lingered in the doorway of the parlour. There was something pitiably appealing in the droop of his moustache.

'Good-bye,' he said softly.

'Good-bye,' said Mrs Bone frigidly.

In the hall Mr Bone collided with Sloley-Jones who had descended the stairs deep in thought. Mr Bone passed him without a word and crept wearily out into the car.

'It is as I feared,' was the parson's report. 'Rotten. I simply cannot for the life of me make out what can have been up. That's no more Mrs Hackett than you are – not so much. Well, perhaps just about as much, to be strictly accurate. There must be some extraordinary mistake somewhere – astounding!'

'Mistake? Poof!' said Mrs Bone.

'Hallo! Where's the car going? I say, it isn't pushing off, is it?' asked Sloley-Jones, striding to the window.

'Ferdinand is going back to London.'

'I say! But what are you going to do?'

'I am going to Rushcombe Fitz-Chartres. So are you.'

'Oh, but, Constance. I simply don't like to do that.'

'I,' said Mrs Bone, 'do not like to do it. It does not promise to be a very pleasant duty for either of us.'

'Oh, but, I say; do you mind if I don't come?'

'You must come,' said Mrs Bone in a monotone. 'You owe it to me and to Sophia. You are my informant. You must be there to witness my charges.'

'Oh, can't we write or something? You know—'

'Write! When the only question is how are we going to get there by the quickest means. Those two men have stood here and lied. I mean to get there while Sophia is still enduring the first shock of finding out that she has been tricked. Then will be the moment for your story.'

'Oh, how dreadful; how perfectly rotten! I protest, Constance. I cannot. This is too much.'

'Why on earth did you follow this man here if you didn't mean to interfere?'

'I didn't know who he was. I don't now. I cannot believe that Mrs Hackett – I think really the idea at the back of my mind was to protect Mrs Hackett.'

'Indeed? She seems to possess a great influence over young men. Well, here is your chance to protect her. You will be with me when I launch my accusation. You can protect her.'

Sloley-Jones groaned and stroked the Adam's apple of his long neck.

'All right,' he murmured at length.

'Now,' said Mrs Bone. 'How far is this town where you live?'

'Downblotton? About five miles.'

'You must take me there. When we get there we can hire a conveyance for the rest of the way.'

Sloley-Jones, who knew the shortcomings of Downblotton, nodded.

'But how are we going to get as far as that?' he asked. 'Can't walk you know. Frightfully tiring.'

'I would run,' said the determined mother, 'if it wasn't going to take too long. As it is—'

She cocked her head thoughtfully towards the road.

'Have you one of those little places behind?' she asked.

'I beg your pardon?'

'On your bicycle?'

'Oh, a carrier. Yes, of sorts. But, my dear Constance, that at any rate is absolutely out of the question. Quite – quite out.'

He surveyed his cousin's figure critically.

'In the first place my bicycle is only two and a half horse-power,' he remarked innocently.

'I will come behind you as far as Downblotton,' said Mrs Bone.

'But, my dear Constance—'

'We will leave my bag and umbrella. I will return here for the night. Come. There is no time to lose.'

'But look here. Honestly—'

'My mind is quite made up,' said Mrs Bone. 'Come out. Mount. Wait. Give me your coat to sit on.'

'There is a little seat there,' said Sloley-Jones nervously. 'But—'

'Mount,' said Mrs Bone.

# CHAPTER XXIV

## Precipitations of Moral Rectitude

England owes her status not to the characteristics of her sons, but to those of her daughters.

True, the sons have frequently been turned loose to perform most of the violent work. But they would never have been capable of performing it had they not been the sons of the daughters of England.

This, like most facts, is ungallant. England, as she is today, may well be regarded as the product of persons of the most disagreeable type.

Nor was Waterloo won on the playing fields of Eton. It was won at the childbed of a large number of big, haughty, rather contemptuous and absolutely indomitable women.

Had Mrs Bone possessed a son, he would have been a very different creature from his father. He would have been a vilely conceited, quite unconquerable young man with rows of war ribbons and no sense of humour.

Only a few women of each generation contribute to their country's weal. The brunettes of the green-room and the garage and the suburban tennis court are merely of re-creative value. For creative value look to your big, stolid blonde. She remains laboriously in the background, as the strong, silent member of an acrobatic troupe receives, ignored by the audience, the skipping posturers on his shoulders. Yes, the history and the destiny of the country are centred in that speciality of ours, the big woman. And Mrs Bone had the hips of a stallion.

The motive which impelled Mrs Bone in reckless pursuit of Peter and his innocent dupe, her daughter, was not vindictive resentment of his lies and treachery. Her motive was rather a subtle satisfaction. From the first she had maintained – had sensed – that Sophia had been the victim of a wicked plot. The plotters should be hunted down, immediately, inexorably; should be shown, to their cost, the ability and the energy of that force which they had unwisely omitted from their calculations. The ponderous cheeks, bobbing and quivering with the vibrations of Sloley-Jones's motorcycle, were flushed with imperious excitement.

The discomforts, and indeed the danger, of her position as she clung, shaken like a cork on the ocean, to the parson on that precarious journey were nothing to Mrs Bone. Had she been swept to Rushcombe Fitz-Chartres on an aeroplane to be dropped at the Knoll by parachute, she would not have faltered. Her thoughts were elsewhere; triumphantly contemplating the discomforts, and indeed the danger, of the outrageous gang she was about to shatter.

That she had been momentarily outwitted at the inn was not unprofitable. Bump! For it incriminated the husband. The husband in fact was a party to this disgusting assignation. Bump, bump! How unthinkably vile! Hoot! One read of such things sometimes in the law reports – Bump! – in the awful sort of chaotic state in which the lower grades of Society found themselves – Ho-oo-oot! – following the war.

At this point Mrs Bone was carried suddenly in a ghastly vertical slither to the extreme side of the road, where, releasing Sloley-Jones, she was slung from the bicycle and alighted, in a sitting posture, on a low bush.

A market cart, which had swerved to the other side of the road in order to escape colliding with the cycle, halted a few yards further up the road. From inside it the heads of the driver, Mrs Spoker, Mrs Wigger, Gladys and the chemist's assistant from Downblotton were craned inquiringly back.

Sloley-Jones, who had retained his seat, relinquished it voluntarily and hastened to the bush.

'My hat! My goodness, Constance, I say I am most awfully sorry. That cart was to blame, you know. Entirely. By Jove, I am sorry. Are you hurt?'

'No,' said Mrs Bone.

'By Jove, I am sorry,' said Sloley-Jones. 'I couldn't absolutely do anything else. The cart—'

'Remove me,' said Mrs Bone.

'Anybody 'urt or hinjured?' asked the driver of the cart.

'Take my hand and give yourself a little sort of heave if you can,' said Sloley-Jones. 'I know it's rather difficult to sort of heave like that out of a bush. No grip, so to speak. I've tried it myself. Sure you're not hurt?'

'Not physically,' retaliated Mrs Bone, vainly heaving.

'I am so beastly sorry,' said Sloley-Jones. 'Now, again. Hup!'

'Any damage?' inquired the cart.

'Not physically, I believe,' called Sloley-Jones. 'Now. Hup! Hup!'

'How can I?' protested Mrs Bone. 'Stop doing that at once.'

'Oh, sorry,' said Sloley-Jones. 'I say, I am frightfully sorry. How awfully rotten for you! Do you think you could sort of worm up by yourself?'

'No,' said Mrs Bone.

'Well, what are we to do? Are you sure you're not hurt? Could you sort of use my shoulders as a lever and work yourself out.'

'No,' said Mrs Bone. 'Leave me alone.'

'I say. You are not too shaken to move, are you?'

'No. Fortunately I am not.'

'Well, I say, do see if you can't try and get out. You simply can't go on sitting in a bush. Do let me have one more try and see whether I can't hoik you out.'

'Wait,' said Mrs Bone. 'I think I am caught.'

'Oh, I see. Oh, well, half a tick. Don't let's tear your skirt. I wonder whether I could sort of oil round underneath you, so to speak, and disentan—'

'Stop!' cried Mrs Bone. 'Go away. I will do it myself. Go right away. Don't watch me.'

'Oh, all right,' said Sloley-Jones. 'By Jove, I am sorry about this. What sickening luck!'

He turned and faced the cart. The occupants had descended and were approaching.

'Hallo! It's Mrs Spoker. How queer. I say, Mrs Spoker, this won't do.'

'Tell those people to go away,' said the voice of Mrs Bone, laborious in gymnastics, from the bush.

'Mrs Wigger, too, as I live! Why, Mrs Wigger, what are you doing here?'

'Will you tell these men to go away?' came in strained accents from the bush.

'Be the lady demmidged?' asked the driver, who was an elderly man with baggy knees and no teeth.

'No, thanks,' replied Sloley-Jones. 'Not hurt. Just caught. She doesn't want—'

'Corrt?' exclaimed the driver advancing. 'Ay. Leave 'er to oi. Oi'll worry 'er free.'

'I don't really think she wants any help, thanks very much indeed all the same. She asked me not to help. I—'

'Go away from me,' cried Mrs Bone in the voice of one purple with effort.

The driver, a noted local Lothario, merely grinned and bared his wrists.

'Don't 'ee straggle now,' he exhorted. 'Oi'll settle 'un. Ye stand by, Robby, and leave 'er to oi. Oi'll worry 'er free.'

Robby, who was the chemist's assistant, stood by with interest. His feminine companions ranged themselves in the background; Mrs Spoker frowning upon the driver's chivalry, Mrs Wigger anxiously smoothing her bonnet strings.

'Cathcart! These men! Will you—? Don't touch me. How dare—'

Leaning forward the driver had seized Mrs Bone by the waist. Her struggles were sporadic but violent, like those of a hen frightened in a coop. Sloley-Jones hovered ambiguously at her side.

'Leave me go. Leave me go!' commanded Mrs Bone.

'I say, leave the lady go. I know it's kindly meant but she

doesn't want— There! By Jove, you nearly had her off. Once more!'

'Cathcart! Order him to stop. You encourage the man. I will not—'

'Oh, let him, Constance. Now, once again.'

'I am being assaulted and you stand by and—'

'No, no, really. It's for the best. You can't go on sitting in a bush. Now! Hup? No. Now again! Hoop!'

'Hup!' echoed Robby.

'Hup!' repeated the driver.

'Stop! Stop this instant! I am being—'

'Hup hup!' said Sloley-Jones encouragingly.

A final struggle. A long-drawn whistle of rent apparel. And Mrs Bone was free.

The driver deposited her on her feet in the road and wiped his brow.

'You great, clumsy rowdy!' cried Mrs Bone; her face disfigured with highly-coloured patches of heat and rage. 'You have torn my dress in halves.'

'Ah, oi 'ad to do that in order to worry 'ee free,' explained the driver.

'Go away, all of you,' repeated the poor lady almost in tears. She turned rampant to Sloley-Jones. 'Idiot!' she added briefly.

'I say, I'm sorry, Constance, but—'

'Sorry you stood by and encouraged?'

'It was kindly meant you know. Frightfully. After all, you were absolutely hung up—'

'My skirt has been lacerated. Send those people about their business all of them.'

'I say, half a tick! Don't be ratty with these people. I know these people. They're awfully decent people. That one is Mrs Wigger, my landlady; and the other is Mrs Spoker, *your* landlady. I know these people.'

'What was that you said?' asked Mrs Spoker sharply.

'Oh, are you there, Mrs Spoker? Yes. This lady is coming back to put up at the *Stag and Hunt* tonight. She—'

'No,' said Mrs Spoker interrupting with decision. 'I am completely occupied.'

'Oh, but surely there is one room? Joking apart, I say.'

'I am not joking,' announced Mrs Spoker frowning heavily. 'I am completely occupied owing to Mrs Wigger, who is returning with me to 'elp nurse.'

'Oh,' said Sloley-Jones blankly. 'I say, Constance, this is rather a snag. Troublesome! I wonder what we'd better—'

Mrs Bone had retired several paces further down the road and was examining the damage to her skirt. The news that she would be unable to return to the *Stag* seemed, if anything, to soothe her slightly.

'You see, sir,' said Mrs Wigger, advancing a little and engaging the parson confidentially, 'Mrs Spoker, 'aving 'eard the old lady was said to be ill, asked me if I could possibly go and, perhaps, lend a 'and. So I 'ardly felt I could do other than do anything else but do so.'

'Yes, I see, Mrs Wigger. Rather. Of course. But how rotten—'

'Not,' interrupted the harsh voice of Mrs Spoker, 'that I am so sure that I should choose in any case to put up ladies who think fit to be seen in the public road riding bicycles bareback.'

Mrs Bone proceeded a few yards further down the road with the air of one avoiding an evil smell.

'Say good-bye to your friends and join me,' she said with great scorn to her cousin.

He returned to her side immediately, expostulating and apologising profusely. The cart party re-formed and continued their journey.

Mrs Bone snapped the chattering Sloley-Jones into silence.

'Now,' she said. 'Is your bicycle intact?'

'My bike? Yes, I saved it. Narrow squeak though. My brakes are rather dud and—'

'Then we will go on,' said Mrs Bone.

'Go on? But, Constance, are you fit?'

'Don't waste time. Remount.'

'Oh, but is this wise? Do you think we really—?'

'We will, at all events, go to the place where you are staying, Oldblotto, or whatever it is called. Take me to your rooms.'

Sloley-Jones adjusted his glasses and inspected the bicycle, which reclined in the hedgerow, very dubiously.

'Honestly, Constance,' he said, 'don't you think it looks – don't you think it looks rather – rather as if we are not *meant* to go on, in a sort of way?'

Mrs Bone really flared up then. She waved demonstrative gloves at Sloley-Jones and his bicycle, and arraigned them in a voice which quivered with fury.

'So,' she cried, 'when you are fool enough to catapult me into a thicket, you have the presumption to explain that it was an act of Divine Intervention. How dare you, Cathcart? I am losing all patience with you. Mount!'

'Oh, I don't go so far as to say—'

'Mount!'

She was full of grit, this matron.

They arrived at Downblotton without further mishap. Their appearance in the town was greeted with spasmodic bursts of enthusiasm by citizens of the lower order. Mrs Bone kept a stiff lip.

In Downblotton town Sloley-Jones was commanded to make inquiries for a vehicle in which to complete the journey. The result confirmed his anticipations. No such vehicle was available. Old Stacey, they were informed, had a goat-carriage which he had obtained from a cousin away down at the sea-side, who had gone broke; but, now their informant came to think of it, there had been some rumour that the goat was dead. Mrs Bone arrived at her cousin's lodgings with temper and spirits sadly impaired.

Here was a letter addressed to Sloley-Jones by Mrs Wigger. It set forth, by a tortuous process of epistolary smoothing, the reason of her absence; during which her lodger's needs were to receive the attentions of Ruby Kettle, of next door.

Mrs Bone soon made herself at home. She routed out Ruby Kettle, whose first duty was, appropriately enough, to serve the wayfarers with tea. Meanwhile a careful examination was made of the damage sustained by the skirt.

This proved to be extensive. At the moment of the accident Mrs Bone's bearskin coat had flown open. In the subsequent worrying free the skirt had been torn to ribbons. The effects of all she had endured at Sloley-Jones's hands, and the contemplation of all that she might be destined yet to endure had already caused the brave woman for the first time to waver. The skirt decided her.

'I will stay here,' she said. 'I will write to Sophia. You will take the letter, and you will bring back Sophia with you, unless these people, the Bunkums, have the decency to provide her with a car. Give me ink and a pen.'

Sloley-Jones provided her with these articles without comment. He placed his spectacles upon his forehead and blew his nose, cogitating as he watched her write. If he raised any objection to going it was a thousand to one that Mrs Bone would devise some devastating alternative. Besides, he rather wanted to go on his own account. He was curious to learn the truth of Mrs Hackett's adventure. Of course he did not for one moment suspect that Mrs Bone's suspicions were justified. But something of a decidedly piquant nature must have occurred.

He was ruefully conscious of a sentiment that even if Mrs Hackett were proved to have behaved in the most naughty fashion, this fact would make her only rather more attractive than otherwise. The charity that thinketh no evil is often difficult to distinguish from the curiosity that thinketh very little good.

Having completed the letter, Mrs Bone arose and handed it to him with a ceremony and finality which he found rather disconcerting.

'You promise me upon your word of honour as a gentle-

man – in holy orders – that you will hand this letter to
Sophia and will not return to me without an answer unless
Sophia herself accompanies you?'

'Righto,' agreed Sloley-Jones glancing at the letter nervously.

'You may read it if you like. It is a plain statement of fact.'

Sloley-Jones read it. His face became graver and graver
during the process. Mrs Bone was watching him eagerly.

'Take it or leave it,' she exclaimed, the moment he looked
up from the page.

'Righto,' sighed Sloley-Jones, folding the letter and placing the envelope in the pocket of his Norfolk jacket. 'But
why take all this trouble to destroy Sophia's happiness with
her husband? I mean to say – even supposing this is true—'

'*Destroy* Sophia's happiness? I am r-rescuing her happiness. The only thing to keep that man straight is a lesson.'

Sloley-Jones turned unwillingly towards the door. He
seemed to be about to continue the argument, but contented
himself with a sigh.

'I ought to change my clothes before I go,' he said.

'Poof,' said Mrs Bone. 'You'd be just as dirty again by the
time you got there.'

'Righto,' said Sloley-Jones. 'Mind you,' he added, turning
in the doorway, 'I may not get there. I've had a great deal of
trouble today already. I may get oiled up. I dare say you
heard, when you were sitting behind me, how I was popping
and the queer sort of twanging noise that was going on in my
valves.'

Mrs Bone 'shoo'd' him out, as the housewife 'shoo's' an
errant hen.

She proceeded upstairs to the private apartment of Mrs
Wigger, where she removed her skirt and inaugurated an
extensive raid for thread and needles.

She went below again and sat in Mrs Wigger's parlour in
her petticoat, stitching.

For hours she seemed to sit and stitch, stitch at her torn
skirt. Her elderly limbs were stiff and weary from the un-

usual experiences which that day had appointed them to
suffer. Ruby Kettle came and went. The head drooped over
the stitching but still the dogged hands worked on as though
mechanically. The impulsive, mettlesome mind began to
wander, to dream.

Dreamt, perhaps, of the long-passed, undisclosed days of
her own youth and of the penurious content of an unambitious suburb, long before the first seductive visions of
wealth and of that chimera, a place in Society. Whatever her
dreams, they seemed to bring the unfamiliar and half-bitter
comfort of human tenderness even to Mrs Bone; for the
heavy eyelids, lowered in frowning determination over the
stitching, were wet.

The long afternoon dragged into evening. The sun
gleamed weakly through the windows of the little parlour
and departed. Shadows fell. But Sloley-Jones returned not
again.

# CHAPTER XXV

# Bad Manners and Evil Communications

Peter did not succeed in presenting his wife with a full and clear statement of the case during their journey in the car. The car had not been built for confidences. Nor did Sophia, who was in an exhilarated frame of mind, invite or encourage any further details of his recent experiences. Peter, after one or two false starts, decided to postpone revelations until after their arrival at the Knoll.

Lady Bunter, who was by this time prepared for almost any eventuality, sustained the appearance of the two simultaneous and apparently cordial husbands, to say nothing of the odd wife, with admirable presence of mind. Sir Stirling, taking his cue from the only reliable prompter, mumbled some rather baffled greetings and retired into the library to hold his head. Margaret was not in evidence, and her husband, who appeared to enjoy some sort of tacit understanding with his hostess in the matter, immediately disappeared without explanation, in search of her.

The homely charm of the dear old lady set Sophia's last fears at rest. The smart country house party faded into the prospect of a complacent holiday in the company of some of the least awe-inspiring people imaginable. True, Mrs. Hackett might prove to be a lady of the challenging type. Already Sophia found it impossible to picture her as anything else. But however smart Mrs Hackett might prove, Sophia felt little misgiving in a house where the hostess treated the announcement that two of her guests had arrived without any luggage as though it were an incident of the most satisfactory, if not usual, nature.

But an hour later found Sophia in her bedroom. She was sitting forward, supporting her face between her hands. She had removed her hat, and her black locks hung over her eyes in a manner which lent a savage comeliness to her appearance. Opposite her, supported by the edge of a dressing-table and in the direct line of fire from those half-hidden, reproachful, searching eyes, stood Peter.

'I want to know why,' Sophia was saying. Her voice was deep and earnest. 'You went out of your way to say that Mrs Hackett was still at the inn. She wasn't. She was here the whole time. What's the point? Why was it necessary for you to lie to me?'

'I didn't mean to lie to you,' said Peter.

'You didn't mean to lie, when you distinctly—?'

'Not to you. I meant to lie, but I didn't mean to lie to you. I only meant to lie to your mother.'

'I want to trust you and to love you,' said Sophia. 'I thought I could. How can I now? I know Mother was suspicious and rather hostile. I dare say you resented that. I did myself. But why lie to Mother even?'

'Oh, dash it all; I had to do that,' said Peter.

'But why? Why?'

'What?'

Sophia rose with an impetuous toss of the hair and a sound like an isolated sob. She walked across the room to the window. From the hall below them Francis' gong cheerfully invited them to drown their sorrows in tea.

Peter remained at the dressing-table, stroking his chin and watching his wife moodily. If she cut up like this over the first paltry item of his confession, how the dickens was he going to tell her all?

'Is that the woman?' asked Sophia suddenly in a hard tone, without turning her head from the window.

Peter crossed the room and joined her. Along the terrace below the window Mr and Mrs Hackett were strolling towards the house door. She was talking quickly and gesticulating lightly with her left hand. Her right lay on his coat-sleeve. Hackett's attitude was that of a doctor, listening with courteous reserve to the patient's statement of the case.

'Yes, that's Margaret – Margaret Hackett,' said Peter. 'You'll like her, you know,' he added sedulously.

'She's older than I imagined,' commented the woman.

'Oh, yes. You'll like her all right,' affirmed Peter.

'He lied too,' said Sophia sharply, frowning beneath her tresses. 'Why? He seemed so nice, I thought. I want to understand why you both lied about her.'

She faced Peter and shook back the hair from her eyes. She stretched a pleading hand out to him.

'I was happy again,' she cried. 'I want to go on being happy, Peter. Is there any other little thing you've been keeping back from me?'

Peter raised his eyebrows speculatively.

'In a way I suppose there is,' he confessed.

'Ah!'

She nodded gladly into his face. He took her hand in his but dropped his eyes.

'Tell me everything.'

'I should love to do that,' he said. 'In fact I've been waiting to. But it's nothing in the least – wrong, and it will take a long time to explain fully and you've got to do your hair and put your hat on again and tea's ready. What about taking a little walk after tea?'

Sophia turned towards the dressing-table.

'Is it anything you're ashamed of telling me?' she asked.

'No, my dear, no.'

'If it is, Peter, tell me. You must trust me.'

'It isn't,' he answered.

'I'm glad of that,' said Sophia, 'though I hope you would keep nothing back in any case. Just tell me the salient points while I do my hair.'

Her nimble fingers were already busy. Peter cleared his throat unnecessarily and glanced at the sharp features in the looking-glass. She was in a restless changeable mood, he thought, a dangerous mood.

'It's rather difficult to pick out the exactly salient points,' he said. 'I missed the train and met Margaret – Margaret

Hackett, and took her in the car – in pursuit of you, of course. You know all that.'

'Yes, yes. And you took Mrs Hackett to the inn. And you all stayed there last night. That was true, I suppose? When did Mrs Hackett come on here? That's what I want to know.'

'Today.'

'How?'

'In the car. Our car. The car we started in.'

'Then the car did not really break down?'

'Oh, yes it did. It broke down but then it broke up again. I mean Dann fixed it up.'

'Dan? Is that Mr Hackett?'

'No. A driver chap.'

'Who came here with Mrs Hackett then? Why didn't you?'

'I did.'

Sophia turned her head. A band of raven hair fell over her cheek and she swept and held it aside as she looked at Peter.

'Lies again,' she said. 'Why did you both tell me these lies?'

'I told you there were more, and we didn't tell 'em to *you*. We told them to Mother.'

'But why tell them to Mother?'

'Because she came down simply boiling over with accusations.'

'Lying to her wouldn't make it seem any less likely,' said Sophia petulantly. 'I'm surprised at Mr Hackett. Why should *he* lie?'

'Oh, thanks,' said Peter. 'I'm quite as honest a man as Hackett. I expect as a rule he lies a great deal more freely than I do. He's an M.P. But, in this case, he lied because he didn't want anybody to suspect his wife's honour.'

'He seems very nervy about it,' said Sophia with sarcasm. 'Besides, there was surely nothing very outrageous in being stranded at an inn for the night. You couldn't help yourselves. Why should Mother have been suspicious?'

Peter rose excitedly and kicked at a footstool.

'She had made up her mind to be suspicious,' he answered. 'She came down today in malice aforethought, full out and breathing through her nose, to try and get me into trouble. If she hadn't been so fiercely punitive I wouldn't have lied.'

'If you'd been a little more harmonious with Mother since we married she would trust you more,' said Sophia, snatching angrily at a falling hairpin.

'I've never known such a woman,' was his reply. 'She's like nobody on earth; for sheer enmity she beats the band. The only people who can hold a candle to her are those Mexican bandits in films, who blow into a township and shoot up the minister just for the joy of making trouble. I'm innocent – incapable, I mean, of anything disgraceful. You believe that. Why can't she? I lied to her simply because I can't trust her to believe the truth. That's probably what makes liars of most – liars.'

'Don't speak like that of Mother,' said Sophia with a quivering lip. 'She did everything for her love of me.'

'I thought she did it for her hate of me,' said Peter.

Sophia rose briskly and snatched her hat from the bed.

'And that, I suppose, in a nutshell, is all?' she asked.

'That's all before tea,' said Peter firmly.

She burst into a passion.

She stamped her foot. She flung her hat away from her. It performed a graceful half-circuit of the room and fell at her feet. She threw herself forward on the bed, her face buried in her hands.

'Sophia! Look here, my dear girl, really—'

Peter's hand was on her shoulder. She shook it off.

'Go away,' she sobbed. 'Go down and have tea with Margaret.'

He hesitated. She raised her face for a moment. It had lost all its attraction and was merely forbidding. Peter made a little appealing movement of the hands, as though offering to raise her.

A minute later he found himself in the drawing-room,

avoiding Margaret's eye and murmuring vaguely at Lady Bunter.

'She's tired, poor dear. She ought to have had tea directly she arrived. How thoughtless and muddling of me.'

Thoroughly in her element, the good lady presently ascended the stairs. In her hand she bore a cup of tea, with slices of bread and butter in the saucer. Lady Bunter had anticipated some such crisis. The hand which bore the tea trembled with anxiety. Indeed, by the time she reached Sophia's room the bread and butter had become positively uneatable except in a humid condition resembling pudding.

Sophia accepted the tea gratefully but declined comfort. She wished to be left quite alone and not to see anybody. No, she didn't want Peter to come up again yet. She was all right, she thought, but had a splitting headache. Lady Bunter was very kind. She understood, didn't she? Sophia was very sorry to collapse like this, but she'd be better soon if she was left to herself.

Lady Bunter did not quite understand, but she said she did. She could only regard the frenzy of this dark, emotional girl with the imaginative pity of the seeing for the blind. She allowed herself to be awed into submission to the younger generation. She told Peter that his wife must be left alone to rest. Peter hung about on the staircase indecisively for ten minutes; then plunged away into the grounds with his hands in his pockets.

It would be hard to determine which of the young couple felt the more injured.

Lady Bunter still hovered on the landing. Margaret joined her at one point, penitent and sympathetic. Should she see the girl? Lady Bunter shook her head decisively. Solitary reflection was the best palliation, she said. 'Palliative, dear,' suggested Margaret. 'Never mind what I mean. Please help me by doing what I say,' replied Fanny.

So Sophia was left to brood alone in her temper and shame. Nobody suspected for a moment that the worst had yet to be told her.

Peter stormed about in woods, hacking at ferns; hacking mentally at the chains which bound Sophia to her dogmatic, proprietary mother. He would fight the old woman this time and for all. He would then take Sophia away – to the Continent or something – and would lull her into a permanent and confident devotion.

He stalked on. The leaves were already falling fast and lay in damp masses at his feet. He kicked them as he walked. At length upon a grassy plateau beneath an oak tree he sank exhausted in mind and body, and tried to regulate the disordered, injured medley of his thoughts.

Yes, Sophia would want some lulling, though. At one moment she had clasped him to her with soft endearments, at the next had flung him from her with weeping and gnashing of teeth. Still, with concentration and opportunity he thought he would be able to lull her all right.

He lay on his back and gazed at the blue sky above him. There was rhyme and reason after all in the old standard music-hall jokes about mothers-in-law. He had married beneath him, that was the trouble. Not that he wanted to go back on Sophia. But her mother might have been discovered in a seaside boarding establishment. All the more reason to stick up to the old devil.

Peter pulled his hat over his eyes.

What a day he had had. Waking in that room in the *Stag* with poor old Margaret in an awful state of panic. Then looking for her little worm of a dog. The car ride here and back again with wind up, only to break down on the road. Fairly running all the way into Downblotton. Oh, that postmaster and his infernal telephone!

Fancy, now the life of that postmaster. Extraordinary how some people were content to go through this world in a groove, seeing nothing of life.

Good Lord, he had left that bicycle at the *Stag*. Couldn't be helped. He'd see about it some time – some time.

How funny Sophia was. There were two of her. He was like that picture of Garrick between the Muses. Only Sophia was both Muses at once, smiling comedy and rabid disfigured tragedy. Were they Muses? Whatever they were anyhow. Garrick it was, wasn't it?

He liked the comedy Muse – woman, whatever-you-call-her best. She had funny people round her. Old Bone and Alfred and a tall, grave man – yes, Hackett, all dressed up in the costumes of cross-talk comedians and exchanging side-splitting banter about kippers. Hackett didn't seem to see anything funny in it. Old Bone had on striped pyjama bags. He did look an ass, but he seemed to be pleased.

There was only one Muse creature now. There had only been one all the time really. Oh, they had left all the other people now and were – where was this? Why, it must be above the bar. Oh, dash it, he couldn't sleep on the floor again. It was so wet. It was wringing wet. She needn't be afraid. He wasn't that sort of person. He only wanted to lull her. Lull her. Lull. Lull.


Lady Bunter met Peter in the hall when he returned. His clothes were untidy, his eyes vacant. Lady Bunter immediately thought that he had been attempting suicide and her hand went to her heart. Fond of trouble as she was, she had had enough for one day.

'Sorry, Lady Bunter,' he said. 'I went out for a walk and sat down under a tree and went to sleep.'

'To sleep? What a one you are for sleeping. You always seem to have been doing something connected with sleeping every time I hear of you.'

'I've had rather a tiring day,' said Peter.

'Yes,' said Lady Bunter. 'So have I.'

'Is Sophie still upstairs? I think I will go to her now.'

'She's gone.'

'Gone?'

'Yes, she – she went.'

'Went? My dear Lady Bunter, where?'

'A parson came. I think he had been here before today. He—'

'That man again?' cried Peter. 'Is he a familiar, or something?'

'Yes, he was rather,' said Lady Bunter. 'But I think he meant to be nice. He is a cousin of yours, you know; by marriage.'

'But what had he got to do with it? Did he abduct Sophia?'

'My dear boy, be careful what you are saying.'

'There's nothing wrong in "abduct",' said Peter.

'Oh, then I'm muddling it with something rather dreadful. But what occurred was this. He brought her a note from her mother. When he saw me, when he first arrived, he asked me to take it to her as he said he had promised her mother that he would give her the note, though he said he thought the mother was wrong in her supposals – things – wrong end of the stick, you know.'

'Yes,' said Peter. 'But *he* needn't talk. Well?'

'I took the note up to her room. When she read it she got much calmer, I thought. But she said it confirmed her worst – things. Of course I told her—'

Lady Bunter gave a little helpless heave of the shoulders.

'I tried to tell her that you had really done nothing actually bad, and that Margaret Hackett was an old friend of mine and quite incapable of it. But it was no good. She said she wanted to go back to her mother. So I tried to find you of course. Fancy going to sleep out there on the grass. I expect you've caught your death of cold; the grass was dreadfully wet. I will get my husband to lend you some underclothes. You really ought to have a bath, if you can with all this on your mind.'

'When did she go?'

'Oh, a long time ago. She went in our car. I had to lend it to her. She asked for it.'

Peter jerked his head towards the drive.

'And the – parson fellow? Did he go with her in the car?'

'Oh, no. He went back on his motor-bicycle thing. I know because I heard him exploding as he went. By the way he implored me to tell him all I knew about last night.'

'And you did?'

'Yes, you see, I thought if he knew that it was all perfectly innocent, he might be able to persuade your wife and her mother so. But I'm afraid he was rather shocked.'

'Not the last shock he'll get,' commented Peter.

'He said he hoped he wouldn't be lugged into it,' said Lady Bunter pleadingly.

'I like that. He's been lugging, himself, all day. But where did Sophia go to, Lady Bunter?'

'I don't know. The car ought to be back by now, so you can ask the chauffeur. Also, I noticed after she had gone, that she had left her mother's letter lying on the floor of her room. I didn't read it of course, but I picked it up. I don't know whether you ought to read it either, but, if you want to go after her and try and make it up, the letter may tell you where she is.'

'Please let me see it,' said Peter.

Lady Bunter fumbled at the pocket of her tweed skirt.

'And where were Mr and Mrs Hackett all this time?' asked Peter.

'They went out again. A friend of ours who is staying here came in from buying some whisky for my husband. He's rather a weak man – well, he's been living in the East, poor man, and of course that makes a lot of difference. But he started to ask Mr Hackett, and Mrs Hackett too, some rather awkward and offensive questions about their movements, so they went out. I only hope *they* haven't gone to sleep on the grass. Still, Mr Hackett has his own underclothes and things here. Here is the letter.'

'Thanks,' said Peter.

He glanced quickly over the closely written page.

'Look here, I'll read it to you,' he said. 'Then you'll be able to form some sort of idea of what I am up against.'

'Only if you think I ought to hear it. And don't forget that

you acted in a rather provoc – what's that word? – way with
poor Margaret.'

'To the pure all things are pure,' said Peter. 'You are pure.
So is Sir Stirling. Absolutely pure, therefore best. So is Hackett. Why can't these people be pure?'

'I think I ought to be able to say something rather clever
about you and Margaret to that,' remarked Lady Bunter.
'But I can't, so don't let's waste time. Read me the letter.'

'This is what Mother says,' observed Peter:

'MY DEAREST CHILD,

'You will have discovered by the time you get this that
all your husband and the other man told us at the inn was
a tissue of Lies.

'I am writing from your cousin, Cathcart Sloley-
Jones's lodgings at Oldblotto. He brought me here on his
motor-cycle throwing me on the way and tearing my skirt
and shaking me or I would have come the whole way to
fetch you.

'He happened to be at the inn last night and your husband was there with the woman alone. She introduced
him to him as hers. Later your husband and the woman
SLEPT in the SAME BED. He happens to know this.

'I am sorry to have to tell you this like this but it is no
use blinking it.

'I got Cathcart to tell me much against his will what I
suspected from the very first. This woman, Mrs Hackett, is
NOTORIOUS. I seem to have heard something about her
before now, he tells me.

'Come back to me at once. Ask Lady Bunthorne to lend
you a car. She cannot refuse. If she does, get up behind Cathcart but make him ride very slowly and not
SWERVE.

'We will consult quietly as to the best course. But what I
say before I repeat. He must not be allowed to think he
can treat you as a mere chattel of his among his other
pleasures. When he has learnt that I shall be content to
bide by your decision.

'My poor child. But I knew it from the first and we must strike while the iron is HOT.

'YOUR LOVING MOTHER.

'P.S. Your father, thank goodness, has gone back to town.'

'Now how am I going to get there?' asked Peter.

'My dear boy,' said Lady Bunter. 'Stay here quietly and have some dinner and change your underclothes and go off there afterwards, when everybody is less excited and muddled.'

'No. I must go now. I – I want her, you see.'

'You dear boy,' said the old lady affectionately. 'You are like your father. But I can't let you have the car yet, can I?'

'I'll walk and meet it,' said Peter. 'Good-bye.'

# CHAPTER XXVI

# His Own Nest

'Where is Sophia?' asked Mrs Bone. 'Why are you so late? You have kept me waiting in suspense all this time. I have had some food and sent the girl, Kettle, away. Why have you been such hours? And where is Sophia?'

'Isn't she here?' replied Sloley-Jones, wiping the dust from his glasses wearily.

Mrs Bone restrained herself as best she could.

'Oh, don't ask me where she is, you – She is not here.'

'Well, she ought to be. Very funny. She started for here ahead of me in a car. Altogether rather rum, this.'

'Ah, she *did* start to come here?'

'Ra – *ther*. In a car.'

'When she had read my letter?'

'Yes.'

'Did she look very upset?'

'I didn't see her. I understand she was resigned. By Jove, it *is* awful. Can't something—'

'You did not see her?'

'No, she was in her room. Lady Bunter negotiated.'

'Where was the husband?'

'Which husband?'

'Her husband of course. Are you trying to be stupid on purpose?'

'Whose husband, Lady Bunter's?'

'No, you fool. I beg your pardon, but it is your own fault. Sophia's husband.'

'Oh, Peter?'

'Sophia's husband.'

'I don't know.'

'He was not with her?'

'With whom?'

'Oh! With Sophia, of course. Did you think I meant with Lady Bunter?'

'Yes.'

'He was?'

'No, I say I thought you meant with Lady Bunter.'

'Arrch! Did you see the man?'

'What man?'

'Arrch! Sophia's husband.'

'No. I told you so.'

'You didn't. So Sophia read my letter and asked for a car and came away?'

'Yes. I told you that anyhow. I say do let me get some grub, will you? I'm awfully done.'

'And her husband didn't get wind?'

'Wind?'

'Yes. Did not discover that she was leaving?'

'No. I say, I'll tell you everything in a mo. Do give me a chance to get a wash and find some prog.'

'I want to know first why Sophia isn't here.'

'She'll be here in a minute. Driver's lost his way perhaps. Does not know the way perhaps. Doesn't know exactly where this house is very likely. She'll be here in a minute.'

'Go out in the road and toot your bicycle as a signal,' said Mrs Bone.

'Oh, Constance, I can't. I'm awfully spent and frightfully upset over all this. That Mrs Hackett. I'd have staked my life on her honour. A welfare worker.'

'You would have lost your life then,' retorted Mrs Bone. 'I'm afraid you must be a very susceptible man, Cathcart. Anyhow I cannot sit here in this suspense. Go and toot.'

Sloley-Jones did as he was bidden with no very good grace. His signal was unanswered. He returned and commenced his meal. Three times during the course of it he was driven into the street to toot. Finally he was stopped and severely cautioned by the Downblotton police-man.

It was Mrs Spoker's hour for her last look round. She took it hastily and returned to the inn, closing the door. She glared suspiciously at a push bicycle which remained leaning against the outer window ledge of the bar. In the hall lay a Gladstone bag and a lady's umbrella. Mrs Spoker sniffed at them, as she had sniffed at them when she had first seen them lying in the parlour, and as she had sniffed at Alfred when he had been unable to throw any light upon them.

Presently Mrs Spoker, descending the stairs from one of her frequent visits of inquiry to Mrs Wigger concerning the life or death of the old lady above the bar, heard the sound of a car drawing up outside the inn. She stood before the door pluming herself. The door was opened by a chauffeur. Mrs Spoker backed a pace. It was not often the visitors to the *Stag and Hunt* had the door held open for them by a chauffeur.

'Are you the landlady?' asked Sophia.

'I am. But I am completely occupied,' said Mrs Spoker.

'I have been here before today. You were out then.'

'Oh,' said Mrs Spoker. 'Then are them things your things?'

Sophia glanced at the bag and umbrella indicated by the bony finger.

'Yes,' she said, after a moment's hesitation.

'Then I must ask you to take them elsewhere because I am completely occupied tonight. There was another lady said she was coming here, who I saw riding on the bicycle of a clergyman who has been a great deal about here these last two days, and I thought they was hers. Are they yours?'

'Hers and mine,' said Sophia. 'I am her daughter.'

'And at *her* age to go bareback,' commented Mrs Spoker. 'So you have called for them have you, Miss?'

'Yes and for something else,' said Sophia authoritatively.

'What else?'

'Information,' said Sophia.

Mrs Spoker's brow darkened.

'As to what?' she asked.

Of her own accord Sophia led the way into the parlour.
Mrs Spoker, too startled by such an unusual display of independence in her *Stag* to protest, followed; and Sophia closed
the door behind them.

'Very queer stories are being circulated about this inn,'
said Sophia, drawing herself up and facing the landlady with
a command which was the legacy of her mother. 'I am con-
cerned in them. You must tell me what I wish to know.'

'Queer stories about my inn?' repeated Mrs Spoker, her
high shoulders rising like a cat's in ominous hostility. 'What
are they and who dares to tell 'em?'

'A gentleman who was here last night – a clergyman, a Mr
Sloley-Jones, is my informant. He says—'

'Him!' cried Mrs Spoker with a snort of contempt. 'He'd
say anything, the sawney.'

'He met a lady and gentleman here. They were staying
here. Did they stay here alone?'

'Do you refer to Mr and Mrs 'Ackett, M.P.?' replied the
landlady with hauteur.

'Yes. At least – Did they stay here alone?'

'Why should I answer such a question?' said Mrs Spoker.
'They *did* stay 'ere alone, if you must know; all but a dog,
drat it, which was with them.'

'You must answer my questions,' said Sophia, 'or I shall be
obliged to send lawyers to you.'

'Lawyers!' cried Mrs Spoker. 'What are you wishing to
imply about the manner in which I conduct my inn.
Lawyers! We are very strict here, allow me to tell you, young
lady. Anythink that is not strictly above suspicion never sees
the light o' day inside o' here.'

'Perhaps you have been imposed upon,' said Sophia.

'I – imposed on? Indeed? I should very much like to 'ear
in what respect,' replied Mrs Spoker with set teeth.

'You are sure that the gentleman who was here with Mrs Hackett last night was really Mr Hackett?'

'Is that what that clergyman 'as bin sayin'?' snapped Mrs Spoker. 'And me takin' as usual all proper precautions in the matter. Is it likely that a M.P. would 'ave such audacity and wickedness?'

'The point is that it may have been some one masquerading as the M.P.,' explained Sophia.

'Masqueradin'! Nothin' of the sort. If you send your lawyers 'ere they'll get a job o' slander against your clergyman friend if 'e don't mend 'is ways.'

'But how can you prove that the gentleman here last night was really Mr Hackett?'

'How can I prove it? Didn't 'e sleep with Mrs 'Ackett, and me as it 'appened by chance, see them at it?'

'Does that prove it?' queried Sophia with a slight quiver of the lip.

'H'm. This is nice from a young lady, I must say.'

Mrs Spoker thrust her chin into the air and turned, scowling, towards the door. Then a thought struck her and she faced round.

'Prove it? You follow me, if you please. You will see whether this will prove it.'

Sophia's eyes brightened. Hope and fear fought within her as she followed Mrs Spoker down the narrow hall into the office.

Mrs Spoker laid her hand upon the large closed register of her guests.

'The names,' she announced, in the manner of a conjuror in his introductory stages, 'is entered in this book accordin' to the law. I saw Mr 'Ackett, M.P., enterin' the names with 'is own 'and with my own eyes. Would an M.P. forge? Per'aps you can recognise 'is writin'.'

'Let me see,' said Sophia quickly.

Mrs Spoker relinquished the ledger with a superior sniff. Sophia opened it and turned anxiously to the latest entries.

'You say you saw – Mr Hackett – write this?'

'He was completin' it just as I come in from shuttin' away the dog,' said Mrs Spoker.

Sophia looked up from the page at the little window pane before her as though she could perceive the figure of Peter, maligned and innocent, awaiting her beyond it. The bold handwriting in the album was certainly not disguised; nor, in any case, could Peter have been capable of so complete and subtle an improvement upon his customary scribble. Sophia closed the book with a jubilant snap.

'Thank God,' she said.

'Whatever you may 'ave discovered, there can be no excuse to be blarspemous,' said Mrs Spoker severely.

Sophia made no reply. She was already in the hall, stooping to take up the bag and umbrella. Mrs Spoker followed her, arms akimbo, working her moustache to and fro querulously.

'And *now*, 'ave you any complaint to make about the manner in which my 'otel is conducted?' she challenged.

'No,' said Sophia. 'No. It must all have been a mistake. Thank you. Good night.'

Her mind was still perplexed with little doubting questions which had still to be explained. 'Where did Peter sleep last night then?' whispered one. 'Why should he say he slept here?' asked another. 'Perhaps there was somebody else and the Hacketts are keeping it dark for him,' suggested a third. Sophia shook them from her head. The one, cardinal fact was proved. Peter had been falsely accused. He had tried, in his poor old blundering way, to tell her all, and she had lost her temper and driven him away unheard.

'Where now, 'm?' asked Wemblow, the chauffeur, with patient anxiety.

'Back, please.'

'Back to the 'ouse, 'm?'

'Yes.'

'Hi! Stop!' shouted Peter. 'Is that Lady Bunter's car?'

Wemblow's sigh was drowned in the deeper sigh of his studded tyres.

'Yessir,' he called back.

'Well look here. Lady Bunter said I might take the car back to Downblotton. I want you to take me to wherever you've just taken Mrs Wykeham. I'm sorry but it's awfully important.'

The door of the car was thrown open.

'Peter!'

'Sophie!'

'Oh, Peter.'

Peter sprang inside. The door closed again. Wemblow cocked his head up philosophically and awaited further orders.

'Sophie, my darling, I want to explain; I want to tell you everything.'

'Don't,' she answered. 'Don't tell me anything now. You can tell me everything some other time perhaps. I only want you again. Oh, Peter, what have I done? Forgive me.'

'Never mind, my dear one,' he said. 'That's all over now, isn't it?'

'Yes, yes. Go on kissing me.'

'Right. But you do really mean it to be quite all over now, don't you?'

'Oh, I promise. Let's forget it.'

'Yes, let's,' said Peter. 'Let's go right away from here by ourselves and forget there was ever anything the matter.'

'You darling! Can we do that?'

'We jolly well will,' said Peter. 'We'll go straight away into Downblotton. There's sure to be a night train. We can write to Lady Bunter and go and see her another time together.'

'Oh, yes,' whispered Sophia. 'Yes, I want to go right away with you alone now.'

'We'll do it,' said Peter. 'What's to stop us? But why were you coming back? Had you thought better of it, Sophie?'

The head against his cheek nodded gently.

Peter kissed her forehead. Then he raised his head and called through the window of the car.

'Can you drop us at Downblotton?' he said.

Wemblow was understood to assent.

'And I am not to tell you all I have to tell you now, am I?' said Peter with a shade of anxiety as they went their way.

'No, no,' said Sophia. 'Some other time. And only then if you want to.'

'Of course I want to.'

'It wasn't anything disgraceful, was it, Peter?'

'No my darling, I promise you that.'

'I almost wish it had been,' she confessed softly. 'Then I could have shown you how I forgive.'

Now there is in Downblotton a Cinema. As the car drew up doubtfully in the market square and Peter descended to make a few necessary inquiries before risking its departure, the first of the two evening performances at this Cinema had just concluded. The natives were wearily trooping from the doors, their minds restored to the sobering spectacle of the familiar streets, after dwelling for two blissful hours in the Nirvana of an American palace, kidnapping heiresses and devouring sandwiches served on wheels. Peter crossed the road and questioned one of the more elderly devotees of Norma Talmadge.

'Dann!' he cried.

' 'Ullo, sir?'

'What are you doing, Dann?'

'Spent all day what with blacksmiths and whatnot on that darned radiator,' replied Dann. 'This *is* a lamentable and one-'orse town, believe *me*.'

'Have you got her patched?'

'Yes,' said Dann. 'I settled 'er this time, sir; but too late to make a start 'ome tonight.'

'Where's the car?'

'In the blacksmith's yard. There ain't even a garridge at this so-called town.'

'Dann. I've got to get back to town straight away. You must take me. I'll make it worth your while.'

'Well, you was very considerate to me when we parted this morning,' reflected Dann. 'So, if you wants me and will continue considerate, I'll do what yer damn well please, sir.'

'This is better,' said Peter, returning to the side of his wife. 'Three quarters of an hour ago I was hoofing along the road and feeling very depressed about it. I have now two powerful cars at my disposal. We will make London tonight, Sophie. The Bunters' car can report our movements to the Knoll. First of all we will eat. We will go in the Bunters' car to a public house and eat and write, and then we will go in Dann's car home. I never hoped to do the thing in such style.'

Fifteen minutes later they sat at meat in the *George and Dragon* Hotel at Downblotton, having returned the conciliated Wemblow to Lady Bunter with a slightly involved covering letter.

'I think,' said Sophia, 'that before I go back with you, I ought just to let Mother know that she needn't worry over us any more.'

'Yes,' said Peter. 'We might let Jones know at the same time.'

'It might save a certain amount of trouble all round. Shall I call at his lodgings and see them?' suggested Sophia.

Peter hesitated.

'You know, I don't think you'd better go,' he ventured. 'If Mother saw you she would probably become very talkative again. If she only saw me it would probably have the very opposite effect. We want to make London by the morning. Shall I go alone and just put things right with them?'

Sophia watched his face with a loving but still somewhat puzzled gaze.

'Well, suppose I write a letter to Mother, saying that we have made it up?'

'Yes,' agreed Peter. 'And that there wasn't really anything to make up.'

'There wasn't, was there, Peter?' asked Sophia keenly.

'Of course not, my darling—'

'Still, there is one thing I do rather want to get at. Mr Hackett was at the *Stag* all the time with Mrs Hackett. I've found out that for myself,' said Sophia with rather pert satisfaction. 'But where really *were* you? Were you there too?'

'I thought we had decided not to have all this now,' remarked Peter softly.

'I just want to know that.'

'Well, I was there most of the time,' said Peter quickly. 'But you see there wasn't another room so I – I had to sleep where I could. I spent part of the night on the floor of one of the rooms, and part in the stables and part in the garden and – one place and another.'

'Oh, but how miserable!'

'Yes it was. I got awfully wet too.'

'Oh, but Peter! How dangerous!'

'Yes it was rather dangerous.'

'But even now I fail to see exactly why you and Mr Hackett shouldn't have told the whole truth about it before.'

'Before, dear?'

'Yes. All those – all that exaggeration about Mrs Hackett being still at the *Stag*, when she wasn't.'

Peter placed his hand gently on hers with a knowing smile.

'I thought I knew the quickest way of getting you to come with me, Sophie.'

'But why shouldn't we have stayed at the *Stag*?'

'Do you wish we had?'

'Not now,' said Sophia.

'Well, there you are, dearie, you've got what you want. I thought I was doing the best thing. Look here, sit down and write your mother a cheery little line and I will find out where Jones lives and will leave it complete with bag and umbrella.'

'This is very awkward,' said Sloley-Jones.

'Awkward!' said Mrs Bone. 'Is that all it is to you, with my child somewhere on the high road, lost in a car?'

'Well, I really don't think it would be any use my going and looking again. I've done it six times. She's sure to be all right in the Bunters' car. No, when I said awkward I meant about us.'

'Us?'

'Yes. If no one else comes we shall be – h'm – yes. I – Constance, do you think it is – what shall I say – all *right*?'

'What are you talking about?'

'I mean – we shall be alone in the house. Rather – I mean – I suppose it is all *right*, isn't it? I mean – ought we to be alone?'

Mrs Bone rose very stiffly and slowly.

'What are you suggesting?' she demanded.

'You can sleep in Mrs Wigger's bed of course—'

'I shall not sleep. I am too anxious. I shall rest upon the bed you speak of. What bed do I understand you to suggest that I shall r-rest upon?'

'Oh, Mrs Wigger's every time. Ra-ther. But, my dear Conny—'

'Conny?'

'Constance, then, if you're so particular—'

'I am very particular,' said Mrs Bone decidedly.

'What I mean is, do you think it is possible for you to stay here tonight without being just a tiny bit injudicious?'

'What is all this?' demanded Mrs Bone. 'Pull yourself together, Cathcart. I scarcely like to think what you are driving at.'

'Don't take offence. I should love you to stay with me, but it just occurred to me that if we were to be alone together here for a night something might come of it; and then I should feel so awfully uncomfortable about it. You too. Probably more uncomfortable than I should.'

'You are mad,' said Mrs Bone heatedly.

'Not a bit. I am only asking your opinion. You know much

better than I do what is considered improper. If we are left alone together here tonight, do you think we shall be proper? I don't.'

'Cathcart! You are not attempting to make suggestions to me?'

'Yes, I'm afraid I am. I did intend to hint—'

'What, what? What, pray, did you intend to hint to me?'

'That people might say just the same things about us as you – as they have been saying about your son-in-law.'

'How dare you draw such a comparison? How dare you suggest that anyone should whisper such scandal about me?'

'You know what people are,' said Sloley-Jones, wiping his nose humbly. 'You know how stories get about.'

'Poof!' said Mrs Bone.

'Just as you like, Conny – Constance. I only hope it will be all right for you in Mrs Wigger's room. You can sleep in my room if you like. I don't mind a bit. I'll sleep in yours – hers.'

'I have seen the room,' said Mrs Bone. 'It will do, under the circumstances.'

'Which room?'

'Your landlady's of course.'

'Oh, right. But – er – what will you wear? I suppose you'll want something to put on – I mean – you know, nightgown.'

'Your landlady has a spare nightgown, I take it?'

'Oh, you take it? Right. Yes, I suppose she has. I don't remember having – yes. No. Righto.'

'I will look and make quite sure that I have all I want,' said Mrs Bone. 'There will still be time to send the girl, Kettle, to borrow anything I require.'

'Oh, right you are,' said Sloley-Jones, accompanying her rather nervously as she again ascended the narrow staircase of the cottage.

Mrs Wigger's room was of modest dimensions and was but sparsely furnished. It scarcely seemed to hold out the promise of being able to satisfy the requirements of so large a lady as Mrs Bone. Sloley-Jones stood and massaged his chin disconsolately as he watched his guest operating chests of drawers and holding an inspection of Mrs Wigger's night-wear, of which the rare specimens were of a red and somewhat raw flannel.

'I say, would you like to borrow a pair of my pyjamas?' said Sloley-Jones.

'No,' said Mrs Bone.

'Because I thought – we wouldn't send out if we could help it. We don't really want to draw attention to our – to the fact that we are spending the night here alone—'

'Stop that!' cried Mrs Bone. 'I am sick of such rubbish. I shall have to send out to try and borrow some linen. Not that I shall sleep. Why can't you have the spirit to go and find Sophia for me instead of following me about the house, murmuring the most loathsome insinuations. Open the door.'

'I say, I'm sorry—'

'Will you open the door. I wish to go downstairs.'

'Certainly. I only – Hallo!'

The rebuked parson had turned to the door which he had allowed to swing to behind him when he had followed Mrs Bone so attentively into the bedroom. He grasped the handle and pushed. Then, with eyes wide and still magnified in width by his glasses, he turned ominously to his guest.

'The door has been locked,' he cried.

Mrs Bone, who seemed not altogether unprepared for some such occurrence, advanced upon him in the most peremptory manner.

'Open that door at once, and kindly desist from trying to be humorous at a time which is most inappropriate,' she commanded.

'Honestly, Const—'

'Open the door!'

'But I can't. It's been locked from outside. The key's outside. Somebody must have come upstairs quietly while we were talking in here and locked it.'

'Stuff and nonsense!' said Mrs Bone. 'Give the door a shake. Locked it! Who can have locked it? And why? It is jammed. Shake!'

The parson shook. He turned again with a piteous little smile of innocent endeavour, and shook his head. Beads of perspiration appeared upon his brow and trickled slowly down on to his spectacles.

'It's locked – some – joke or something. I – wonder—'

'Shake again,' said Mrs Bone. 'Shake. Have you no strength in your arms? Let me come.'

'Do, do. See if you can do it. I bet you don't do it, but come and can if you do. Do if you can. There you are. Isn't it absurd? I wonder who on earth can have—'

Mrs Bone, spent with a brief but violent wrestle with the door, wheeled upon him, quivering with wrath.

'You arranged this,' she cried.

'I – I swear. Conny, you mustn't say such things. I—'

'Who locked that door?'

'How can I tell? Somebody must have sneaked in from the road and done it for a joke. Most reprehensible. I can't think—'

'We must get out at once.'

'Well, I don't see how we're going to.'

'We must. You do not suggest that we are to be imprisoned here all night, or until Sophia comes?'

'No, I – I – I don't suggest it. That is, I don't desire it. Not the smallest bit. But I don't see how we're going to get out.'

'Make noises,' said Mrs Bone. 'Arouse the neighbours. Make noises.'

'No, no, I say, don't. I shall be made a laughing-stock. So will you. Worse. Gossip. You know what people are. Oh, what miserable luck! Don't let's lose our heads and do anything we might be sorry for.'

Mrs Bone retired to the bed and flounced upon it, shaking in every limb with fatigue and rage. Sloley-Jones, removing and wiping his spectacles, regarded her feebly.

'Well,' she cried at length. 'Do you intend to stay all night in this room with me?'

'Oh, don't,' he replied faintly.

'Unless you exert yourself at once I shall shriek for the neighbours.'

'Oh, I say, don't do that. They'd – they might think I was – taking ad – doing something – One half tick. I'll try and bust the door open, but it will probably make an awful row and attract attention.'

He turned unwillingly again to the door, hesitated, and again faced Mrs Bone, wetting his lips deliberately.

'I – I suppose it *is* the only thing to do? I mean, I suppose we couldn't possibly – No. Oh, dear! Yes.'

He took a very short run and jolted the door half-heartedly with his left shoulder. Beyond the slight noise of the concussion the attack was altogether without result.

'Push, push! Harder!' commanded Mrs Bone.

'Oof! Bah! Oof!' cried Sloley-Jones, trying again.

'Harder, harder!' exhorted Mrs Bone.

'Oof! Kahr! Erph! Oof! I say, don't make too much noise, Constance. We don't want people to hear, do we? I mean, you know what people are. Ooof! It's no good.'

# CHAPTER XXVII

## Other Birds' Nests

When Peter, having found the cottage of Mrs Wigger open to any member of the public who cared to investigate it, had strolled noiselessly into the front parlour, he had been surprised. The room was unoccupied, but there were signs that Sloley-Jones had been there. The parson's evening meal had evidently been consumed there not long before. A portion of it remained on the floor, another portion on the sideboard.

Peter placed the bag and umbrella on the floor of the parlour. He fingered the note which Sophia had written to her mother and cast his eye over the little room. Finally he placed the note in a prominent position on the centre table. As he did so he raised his head quickly.

Next moment he was ascending the stairs with much care. He tiptoed his way stealthily forward until he stood without the closed door of Mrs Wigger's bedroom. A smile flickered over his face as he bent forward to catch the fragmentary conversation which proceeded from within.

Peter straightened himself for a moment. He glanced downwards as though in response to a sudden intuition. Yes, the key happened to be on the outer side of its lock. His hand stole downwards. The temptation was almost irresistible.

A temptation which would be almost irresistible to another youth was altogether too much for Peter Wykeham.

He was quickly back in the parlour. The remnants of the fire, which Ruby Kettle had been commanded to kindle against the chill of evening, still smouldered. Peter stirred it into a little blaze and refreshed it with the note which Sophia had written to her mother.

Then he left the cottage and returned briskly to the *George and Dragon* inn.

'You haven't been long,' said Sophia gladly.

'No, I cut it short. Now, is Dann ready?'

'Yes, waiting. It will be lovely driving back to London with you, Peter. By the way, did you see Mother?'

'Oh, by the way, no, I didn't,' said Peter. 'She'd gone to her room. But I made it perfectly all right. I don't think she'll go on worrying so much about what happened last night now. Nor will Jones.'

'But nothing really *did* happen last night, did it?' asked Sophia with a thoughtful smile.

'Of course not,' replied Peter. 'Where's Dann?'


When Mr Bone arrived at Paddington his eyes wore a look of fascinated indulgence. He gripped his umbrella firmly by the middle, and was borne in a taxi to a small restaurant in the neighbourhood of Soho. He had dinner.

With his dinner he had two deep stoops of sparkling Lager beer. After his dinner he ordered a liqueur brandy. His eyes glistened with a strange light now. He had another liqueur brandy. He had three.

He paid his bill recklessly, looking past the *garçon* into the London night beyond the curtained doorway of the restaurant with a glassy smile. He seized his hat, coat and umbrella from the *garçon*, and rose.

He still gripped his umbrella by its middle portion. With his heavy moustache hanging over a savage grin, and his shoulders bent as though he were crouching for cover, he looked like some untamed cave-dweller of the Neolithic age, stalking forth into the night, seeking what he might devour.

He slung his coat over his left arm. Some object flew from the pocket and skidded, with a rattling noise which startled the diners, along the parquet floor of the restaurant. He took no notice. His eyes were piercing the prospect before him, bright with an enthusiasm which had lain dormant beneath those heavy lids for many a year.

As he pushed aside the curtain, a waiter rescued the object

which he had dropped from the skirts of a vexed female diner, and came running with Gallic cries to restore it to its owner. It was a hairbrush. Mr Bone nodded his acknowledgments with a little grunt, and struck forth into the night.


'Hallo, darling,' murmured Peter. 'I thought you were asleep.'

'I was,' said Sophia, nestling to him again inside the spacious limousine, which bore them smoothly homewards through the night.

'Cuddle down to me,' said Peter, 'and I will lull you.'


When Lady Bunter received Wemblow's despatch, and learnt that the young couple had met, had settled their differences, and had proceeded together to town, whence they hoped they might be allowed to visit her again at a more convenient season, she displayed her satisfaction at this latest victory over trouble by retiring to her bed and sleeping off her fatigue, in readiness for any trouble that might arise next day.

Mr Mock, too, was early asleep and was very shortly afterwards in bed.

Mr Goodie was, like many of the more exasperating of his race, an airly raiser. So he went to bed airly.

Sir Stirling told the Hacketts not to hurry on his account. So the Hacketts went to bed too.

'Poor little people,' said Margaret from the bed. 'I'm glad they have gone off happily together. Thank goodness Sophia came round. I only hope and trust that nothing more may come of my silliness.'

Hackett, standing at the window and looking out into the moonlight, turned with the gleam which was his smile.

'Come what may,' he said, 'nothing can change what we hold dearest, can it?'

'Nothing,' she whispered. 'But, oh, my dear, how lucky we

are. I don't think other husbands and wives can rely on each
other as we do.'

He nodded gravely.

'Perhaps love is rare,' he said. 'Nothing can shake perfect
trust, because trust perfected is truth. Love is truth.'

Margaret kissed her hand to him happily.

'It was really Pansy's fault,' she reflected.

Hackett's manner changed. He seemed, for the moment,
almost apprehensive.

'By the way,' he asked, 'where is Pansy tonight?'

'Sleeping with the spaniel,' said Margaret.

**THE END**